COME GIE'S A SANG

73 Traditional Scottish Songs

edited and annotated by *Sheila Douglas*

with music transcription by *Jo Miller*

foreword by Hamish Henderson

The Hardie Press

CONTENTS

The publisher acknowledges subsidy from the

Scottish ▲rts Council

towards the publication of this volume

© The Hardie Press, 1995

ISBN 0 946868 15 8

First published in Great Britain 1995 by
The Hardie Press, 17 Harrison Gardens, Edinburgh EH11 1SE

Printed in Great Britain by Hobbs the Printers, of Totton, Hampshire

ACKNOWLEDGEMENTS

The editor and publisher wish to express their gratitude to the following: Mary Affleck, Angus Branch TMSA for old festival programmes, Colin Douglas for assistance with textual transcription, Peter Hall for information on singers, Dr Hamish Henderson for help, advice and information on songs and singers, Brian Miller and Pete Shepheard for the right to use their transcriptions of songs nos. 61 and nos.27 & 37 respectively. Thanks are also due to Ailie Edmonds Munro and Scottish Cultural Press for permission to include material from *The Democratic Muse - Folk Music Revival in Scotland* (formerly known as *The Folk Music Revival in Scotland*)

The illustration on the cover is reproduced from a watercolour (1994) by Wendy de Rusett commissioned especially for this publication

The Traditional Music and Song Association (TMSA) of Scotland is a non-profit organisation which exists to promote interest in, and performance of, traditional Scottish music and song. It runs festivals, concerts, ceilidhs, workshops and competitions all over Scotland, all year round. The TMSA enjoys the patronage of Scottish musicians Evelyn Glennie, Barbara Dickson, Billy Connolly and Aly Bain.

Recent TMSA projects have included the Young Champions tour with Aly Bain (highlights of which are available on cassette and CD from Springthyme Records); the Nineties Collection Competition to encourage new compositions in traditional style; and the HARP project in Grampian Region, one of a number of initiatives promoting involvement in traditional arts among younger people.

Preparation of this song book was commissioned by the TMSA to commemorate the Association's Silver Jubilee: twenty-five very successful years. If you would like to help us in our second quarter-century, you can lend direct support by becoming a member. Information about membership, or about affiliation by organisations with similar aims, can be obtained from:

TMSA National Office
Level 3
Greenside House
25 Greenside Place
Edinburgh EH1 3AA
Scotland

FOREWORD

Although Scotland has never lacked for popular song books – and indeed, in the Victorian era, there was a plenitude of them – the vast majority of those published prior to 1950 or thereabouts hardly did justice to the rumbustious, gallus song tradition kept alive and flourishing down the years by the oral tradition.

In the 18th century, one major collection – David Herd's *Ancient and Modern Scottish Songs,* called by Sir Walter Scott "the first classical collection of Scottish songs and ballads" – did put on record the virile reality of the song-treasure he and his contemporaries had inherited and Herd himself was in no doubt about the value of the material he had gathered. In his preface he wrote :-
"The Scots yield to none of their neighbours in a passionate attachment to their native music; in which, to say the truth, they seem to be justified by the unbiased suffrage of foreigners of the best taste, who have candidly allowed it a preference to their own... The merit both of the poetry and the music of the Scots songs is undoubtedly great; and the peculiar spirit and genius of each is so admirably adapted to each other, as to produce when conjoined, the most enchanting effect on every lover of nature and unaffected simplicity."

Of the songs to dance tunes – universally popular then as now – he observed:-
"There is another species, to wit, the humorous and comic, no less admirable for genuine humour, sprightly naïveté, picturesque language and striking paintings of low life and comic characters; the music whereof is so well adapted to the sentiment, that any person of a tolerable ear upon hearing it, feels a difficulty in restraining a strong propensity to dance."

Robert Burns's famous bawdy collection *The Merry Muses of Caledonia* and Peter Buchan's Aberdeenshire equivalent *The Secret Songs of Silence* supply the authentic words for a number of these sprightly tunes, and even Herd – whose collection circulated widely among all classes – wasn't sweir to print lines like:-

> Logan-water and Logan braes –
> I helped a bonnie lassie on wi her claiths;
> First wi her stockings and then wi her shoon;
> And she gave me the glaiks when a' was done.

> But had I kend what I ken now
> I should have banged her belly fou,
> Her belly fou and her apron up;
> And hae showed her the way tae Logan-kirk.

Now turn to any typical song-collection of Victoria's day, and the contrast could not be greater; a sickly-sweet sentimentality is everywhere pervasive, and the same titles tend to re-appear over and over again : "Yon wee Bit Heather" ... "There Grows a Bonnie Briar Bush" ... "The Bluebells of Scotland" ... The irony is that some of the best-known of these cloying ditties turn out, on closer inspection, not to be Scottish at all – or only peripherally so. For example, the last-named – quite a charming little song, one must admit – is to an English air adapted and popularised on the stage at Drury Lane by an Irish actress whose stage name was Mrs Jordan. The words most commonly sung were written by Mrs Grant of Laggan, but there are several versions, all pretty mediocre. In short, it is the sort of song which the modern Revivalist feels instinctively could well be given a rest.

In the 19th century, however, songs of this nature were the staple of countless drawing-room soirées, and they were, of course, almost invariably sung to piano accompaniments; as often as not, the singers would do their best to simulate a high-pan *bel canto* delivery.

One of the many services the present day folksong revival has done Scotland has been to sweep away this rather off-putting anachronistic scene.

If, as Philip Larkin averred, sex began in 1963, Folksong – as thousands of Scots folk know it – began in 1951. This was the year the Edinburgh Labour Festival Committee laid on a fabulous Ceilidh, as part of the first Edinburgh People's Festival, and an enthusiastic audience of predominantly young folk realised with delight that Scotland was still the proud possessor of hundreds of splendid folk artists who had preserved an older singing tradition intact. Since then, the songs that had been living on the lips of tradition-bearers from Buchan to the Borders have become the shared patrimony of a new generation of folksingers, and at folk festivals all over Scotland songs get passed from one singer to another – and as like as not, altered, and quite possibly improved in the process.

The book you have before you is a child of the folk process generated by the post-1950 Revival. All the songs have been transcribed from the singing of people who, in one way or another, have been a part of that movement, and so these transcriptions have a freshness made possible by this direct living connection. This is how someone, somewhere, has actually breathed life into a song!

As will be seen from the biographical notes, the singers from whose repertoires these songs have been drawn range from veteran heroes and heroines like Willie Scott, Jeannie Robertson and Jimmy MacBeath to more youthful champions from the 'second wave' of the Revival like Jimmy Hutchison, Heather Heywood and Peter Fairbairn. The distinction earlier made - by academics, rather than by the singers themselves - between the traditional singers and Revivalists has now largely disappeared : to that extent the Revival presents a united front to the world and exhibits the same homogeneous camaraderie as the folk scene or the Cape Club (Herd's club) and the Crochallan Fencibles (Robert Burns's club). "We're a' Jock Tamson's bairns!"

Incidentally, it has been well-said that a really flourishing folk scene – like ours – is one in which a mother learns songs from her daughter!

The debt which the Revival owes to the TMSA is quite incalculable, and this book stands as a monument to the voluntary efforts of hundreds of members and supporters of the Association who have done their best to honour Scotland's matchless folk heritage in the present century. I have no doubt it will serve as a springboard for many new generations of 'folkies' in the years to come.

HAMISH HENDERSON

EDITOR'S INTRODUCTION

Traditional songs are, by definition, those handed down from one generation to another: just as they are present in every other culture in the world, so they are also part of our national identity. In the past, this heritage has been kept alive by oral transmission but song books and songsheets and, more recently, recordings, have played a part also. Those cultures which have lost their songs have done so through neglect, social and political upheaval or modern influences such as the mass media. We are fortunate in Scotland in having had, even in this century, singers who have some connection with oral tradition, so graphically and joyously described by Hamish Henderson. His work has done much to increase our knowledge of it and I, and others like me, aspire to follow in his footsteps.

In Scotland we have a song tradition that, as well as being highly thought of by the rest of the world, has unique features that differentiate it from all other European traditions, except the Irish. Folk song is usually associated with "the peasantry" or "the working class", but Scottish tradition is shared across the social spectrum with ballads composed by kings and gentry as well as by people of humbler status; songs were made by poets who were also collectors, by farmworkers, fishermen and miners: people from all walks of life sing, a fact to which this book bears witness.

We also have a more bookish tradition, in that many of our ballads and songs have gone in and out of print down the centuries, without destroying the oral tradition which has kept them alive. There is an impressive list of song collections to illustrate this, made mainly by literary men – from Bishop Thomas Percy in the 1700s to Gavin Greig and James Duncan this century – most of whom thought they were rescuing the last relics of something that was dying. There have also been thousands of song sheets sold to the public since the 18th century. I hope this book will be a part of that process, described by Hamish Henderson as "a carrying stream" that picks up and discards but never stops flowing.

Traditional songs often use traditional tunes, new words having been put to airs with which the listeners will be familiar, thus making for continuity as well as ease of transmission. There are also tunes whose source is unknown but are probably original. The transcription of the melodies was undertaken by Jo Miller, whose explanatory notes follow. Singers have always had the right to use whatever tune they wanted and for that reason some songs are known to more than one tune.

Characteristic features of folksong lyrics include formulaic language, repetition for emphasis, sets of three, question and answer forms and so-called 'floating' verses, that turn up in several different songs, like the regretful, "I wish,

I wish, but I wish in vain," of the abandoned lover, and "As I roved out on a May morning" that often begins a love song. The ballads, or storytelling songs, which are among our oldest, are now believed to have been composed orally – a concept hard for us to understand, with our emphasis on literacy – and shaped by recreative performance, as so many of the songs in this book have been. Indeed, this book gives a unique insight into the recreative process in action. Ballads from broadsides tend to feature language that is a mixture of the literary and the colloquial, while bothy songs tend to express themselves in a more down-to-earth style. Music hall songs have a language in keeping with stage entertainment, although the earlier material is relatively free of the "tartan rubbish" syndrome that so seriously afflicts its present day equivalent. There is plenty of humour, but the recurring quality in all the songs is that rare lyricism for which Scots tradition is universally admired.

As collections like that of Francis James Child and Greig-Duncan show, traditional songs exist in many versions – the hallmark of a living tradition. There are, of course, other versions of the songs in this book. In fact, every traditional singer sings songs in his or her own way. There is no question of singers being obliged to adhere to one set of words and notes. The individual versions included in this book are not to be regarded as authoritative; they are descriptive rather than prescriptive, providing material to be used creatively by other singers. Song tradition is a very fluid thing and the message to anyone using this book has to be, "Feel free to change things." Having said that, in order to learn a song, singers should become familiar with the words and the rhythm of the words, as well as singing through or playing over the melody, before trying out a verse, matching the words to the tune. For the follow-on verses, tunes have often to be rephrased or adapted to fit the words, rather than making them a strait-jacket into which singers have to force words in an unnatural-sounding way. This requires a certain skill but it is one most singers develop very quickly and naturally. In many cases, the tune transcription of the first verse shows how the singer has done this. Where a song appears with decorations these should not be copied slavishly by other singers: it is up to the individual singer whether he or she wants to add decoration to express feeling.

I chose carefully words from recordings or from old festival programmes, or in some cases, got them from the singers themselves. As regards their spelling, I observed several points. The Scots language and the song tradition are both characterised by variety rather than uniformity, since there are no standardised forms; so to be consistently accurate I had to preserve the pronunciation of individual singers who come from different areas of the country, use different forms of Scots and mostly sing the way they talk. Some words appear in two spellings in the glossary, for example "aa" and "aw" and "hert" and "hairt", but spelling within a song is consistent to represent that particular singer's accent. I followed one or two rules for the sake of simplicity: no apostrophes are used to indicate "missing" letters (since letters are not missing in Scots words like "wi" and "hielan") and the first personal pronoun is invariably written as "I" even though some singers give it the Scots pronunciation, "A". I regarded *The Concise Scots Dictionary* and *English-Scots Dictionary* as authoritative sources for spellings and took the advice of their editors. There is no lack of spelling guidelines devised by both individuals and groups, but these tend to reflect the subjective judgments and personal tastes of their authors. Even the *Scots Style Sheet* drawn up in 1947 by the Makars Club was a list of recommendations made by writers for literary purposes, whereas most of the songs in this book are closer to oral tradition and the voices of those who sang them.

The singers sang at festivals and ceilidhs run by the TMSA over the past quarter century and I carefully selected the songs to reflect different categories of song and different areas of the country. I aimed to produce a popular song book which anyone cán use and included classic ballads, broadside ballads, music hall songs and bothy songs, love songs, laments and political songs. I gave one example, in a special appendix, of a full transcription of all the verses of a song 'Belt with colours three', as sung by a virtuoso traditional singer, Alison McMorland, transcribed by Ailie Munro in her book *The Folk Music Revival in Scotland*. Many of these songs can be heard on records and tapes currently available, such as Greentrax Records' reissue of the Scottish Tradition series from the sound archive of the School of Scottish Studies.

I intend in the book to give recognition and honour to the many singers who keep our songs alive and encourage us to do the same by singing them. I wish to record my personal thanks to all the singers and their relatives, who gave me words, tunes and biographical information, without which this book could not have come into existence. I am also grateful to the TMSA for affording me the privilege of editing it and to those members who made my task easier. I hope it provides singers all over Scotland and beyond with the means to respond whenever there goes up the cry, "Come gie's a sang!"

SHEILA DOUGLAS

NOTES ON MUSIC TRANSCRIPTIONS

The sources for the transcriptions fall into three groups:-
    (a) Commercially available recordings.
    (b) Recordings made privately by the editor and others.
    (c) Where (a) and (b) are unavailable, the editor is the source. She has
        recalled versions as sung by the singers in question.

The transcriber's job is one of compromise, since not all aspects of song performance (such as tone of voice) can be represented by musical notation. Notation can be used either to set down what is to be performed or to describe what *has been* performed. The transcriptions in this collection try to strike a balance between the two, providing accessible versions of the songs for those who wish to learn them, while also sharing something of the varied singing styles of the singers represented here.

While some songs are shown at their actual pitch as sung in the recordings, many have been transposed into keys which, in the transcriber's opinion, most singers should find comfortable.

Key signatures here are not necessarily a guide to the keynote of the particular song, but show only the actual pitches used. Thus, where F# appears as the key signature, the keynote could be G, but may equally be D, with the melody omitting the C#.

The largest group of songs employs a time signature which applies throughout, and indicates a fairly regular pulse and phrasing (e.g. No 15). A second group of songs has a strong underlying fluidity (e.g. No 12). I have suggested this by using alternating time signatures. Two songs (Nos 9 and 28) are sung very freely, and this is shown by the use of half, rather than full, barlines in the transcription. Rests indicate where the singer takes a breath or completes a phrase.

Unless indicated otherwise, the chorus is to be sung after each verse of a song.

JO MILLER

1. Johnnie Armstrang

sung by Willie Beattie, Caulside, Canonbie

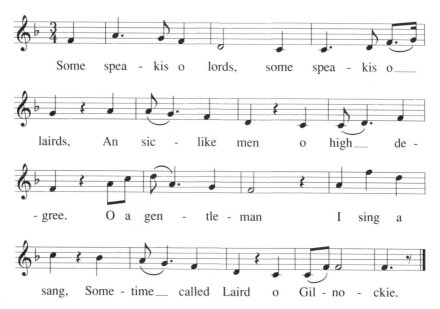

Some spea - kis o lords, some spea - kis o____ lairds, An sic - like men o high____ de - gree. O a gen - tle - man I sing a sang, Some - time____ called Laird o Gil - no - ckie.

2. The king has written a loving letter
   Wi his ain hand sae tenderlie.
   He has sent it to Johnnie Armstrang
   To come an speak wi him speedilie.

3. The Elliots and Armstrangs did convene;
   They were a gallant companie.
   "We'll gan an meet our royal king
   An bring him safe to Gilnockie."

4. "Mak kinnen an capon ready then
   And venison in great plentie.
   We'll welcome hame our royal king,
   I hope he'll dine at Gilnockie."

5. When Johnnie came before the king
   Wi aa his men sae brave tae see,
   The king has movit his bonnet tae him:
   He weened he wis a king as well as he.

6. "May I find grace, my sovereign liege,
   Grace for my loyal men an me,
   For my name is Johnnie Armstrang
   And subject of yours, my liege," says he.

7. "Away, away, thou traitor strang,
   Out of my sight thou mayst sune be;
   I granted never a traitor's life
   And now I'll not begin wi thee."

8. "Grant me my life, my liege, my king,
   And a bonny gift I'll gie tae thee:
   Full four and twenty milk-white steeds
   Were aa foaled in a year tae me."

9. "Away, away, thou traitor strang,
   Out of my sight thou mayst sune be;
   I granted never a traitor's life
   And now I'll not begin wi thee."

HP 17.95

10. "Grant me my life, my liege, my king,
    And a brave gift I'll gie tae thee:
    All between here and Newcastle town
    Shall pay their yearly rent tae thee."

11. "Away, away, thou traitor strang,
    Out of my sight thou mayst sune be;
    I granted never a traitor's life
    And now I'll not begin wi thee."

12. "Tae seek het water aneth cauld ice -
    Surely it is a great folie.
    For I have asked grace of a graceless face,
    But there is nane for my men an me.

13. "Had I my horse an harness guid
    And riding as I wont tae be,
    It shall hae been tauld this hundred year,
    The meeting of my king an me.

14. "Fareweel, thou bonny Gilnock Hall,
    Where on Eskside thou standest stout.
    Gin I had but seven mair years,
    I wad hae gilt it round about."

15. John murdered was at Carlin Rigg
    Wi aa his gallant companie,
    But Scotland's hert was ne'er sae wae
    Tae see sae mony brave men dee.

16. Because they saved their countrie dear
    Fae Englishmen: nane were sae bauld
    When Johnnie lived on the Borderside,
    Nane o them daur come near his hauld.

4

2. Achanachie Gordon

sung by Joe Rae, Beith

"Ach - a - na - chie__ Gor - don is__ bon - ny and__ braw,_____ He would tempt o - ny__ wo - man__ that__ e - ver he saw. He would tempt o - ny__ wo - man_____ sae has he temp - ted__ me,_____ And I'll dee if I__ get - na my love Ach - a - na - chie."

2. In come her faither steppin owre the floor,
   Says, "Jeannie, ye are trying the tricks of a whore.
   Ye're carin for them that cares naethin for thee,
   Ye maun mairry Saltoun, forget Achanachie.

3. "Achanachie Gordon he is but a man,
   Although he be pretty, whaur lies his free land?
   Saltoun's houms they lie bonny, his toors they stand hie,
   Ye maun mairry Saltoun, forget Achanachie."

4. "Ye that are my parents to church you may me bring,
    But unto young Saltoun I'll ne'er bear a son;
    For a son or a daughter I'll ne'er bow my knee
    And I'll dee if I getna my love Achanachie."

5. When Jeannie was mairrit from church was brocht hame,
    When she and her maidens sae merry should hae been,
    When she and her maidens sae merry should hae been,
    She called for a chamber to weep there her lane.

6. "Come to bed, Jeannie, my honey and my sweet,
    For to style you mistress I do not think it meet."
    "Mistress or Jeannie, it's aa yin tae me,
    For in your bed, Saltoun, I never will be."

7. Oot spak her faither, he spak wi renown,
    "Some o you that are her maidens, ye'll loose aff her goun,
    Some o you that are her maidens, ye'll loose aff her goun,
    An I'll mend the mairriage wi ten thoosand croon."

8. Then yin o her maidens they loosed aff her goun,
    But bonny Jeannie Gordon she fell in a swoon,
    She fell in a swoon low down by their knee,
    Saying, "Look on, I dee for my love Achanachie."

9. That very same mornin Miss Jeannie did dee
    And hame came Achanachie, hame frae the sea.
    Her faither and mither met him at the yett.
    He said, "Where is Miss Jeannie that she's nae here yet?"

10. Then forth cam her maidens aw wringin their hauns,
    Sayin, "Alas for your stayin sae lang frae the land,
    Sae lang frae the land and sae lang frae the fleed,
    They hae wedded your Jeannie and noo she is deid."

11. "Some o you that are her maidens, tak me by the haun,
    An show me the chamber that Jeannie dee'd in."
    He's kissed her cauld lips that were caulder than stane
    An he's dee'd in the chamber that Jeannie dee'd in.

3. The Baron o Brackley

sung by Anne Neilson, East Kilbride

Doon Dee - side cam__ In - ver - ey whist - lin and play - in, An he was at__ Brack - ley's yetts ere the day was da - win. "O__ are ye there__ Brack - ley and are ye with - in?__ There's__ shairp swords are at yer yetts will gar yer bleed spin."

2. "Then rise up my Baron and turn back your kye
   For the lads frae Drumwharran are drivin them by!"
   "Oh how can I rise up and how can I gyang?
   For whaur I hae ae man I'm sure they hae ten."

3. "But rise up Betsy Gordon and gie me ma gun,
   And tho I gyang oot, love, sure I'll never come in.
   Come kiss me, my Betsy, nor think me tae blame,
   But against three and thirty, wae's me, whit is ane?"

4. When Brackley was mounted and rade on his horse,
   A bonnier baron ne'er rade owre a course;
   Twa gallanter Gordons did never sword draw,
   But against three and thirty, wae's me, whit is twa?

5. Wi their dirks and their swords they did him surround,
   And they hae slain bonny Brackley wi mony's the wound.
   Frae the heid o the Dee tae the banks o the Spey,
   The Gordons shall mourn him and ban Inverey.

6. "O cam ye by Brackley's yetts or cam ye by here,
   And saw ye his lady a-rivin her hair?"
   "O I cam by Brackley's yetts and I cam by here,
   And I saw his fair lady, she was makin guid cheer.

7. "She was rantin and dancin and singin for joy,
   And she vowed that very nicht she wad feast Inverey.
   She laughed wi him, drank wi him, welcomed him ben,
   She was kind tae the villain wha had slain her guidman."

8. Throu hedges and ditches ye canna be sure,
   But throu the woods o Glentanar ye will slip in an oor.
   Then up spak the babe on the nanny's knee,
   "It's afore I'm a man, avenged I'll be!"

4. The Beggar Laddie

sung by Allan Morris, East Kilbride

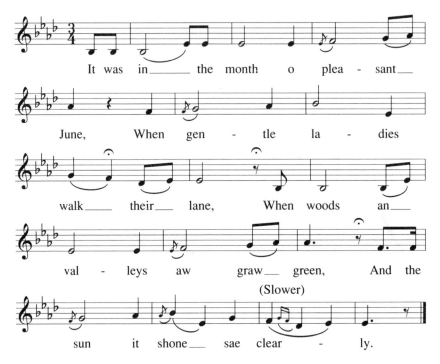

It was in___ the month o plea - sant___ June, When gen - tle la - dies walk___ their___ lane, When woods an___ val - leys aw graw___ green, And the

(Slower)

sun it shone___ sae clear - ly.

2. Doon in yon grove I spied a swain
   A shepherd, sheep club in his hand.
   He was drivin yowes oot owre the knowes,
   And he was a weel-faured laddie.

3. "Come tell tae me whit is your trade,
   Or by whit airt ye win your breid,
   Or by whit airt ye win your breid,
   When herdin ye give owre ?"

4. "Makin spindles is my trade
   And findin sticks in time o need,
   For I'm a beggar tae my trade,
   Noo lassie, could ye loe me?"

5. "I could loe ye as many fold
   As Jacob loed Rachel of old,
   As Jesse loed his cups of gold -
   My laddie, if ye'd believe me."

6. "Then ye'll tak aff your robes o reid,
   And ye'll pit on the beggin weed,
   And ye'll follow me hard at the back
   And ye'll be the beggar's dawtie."

7. And when they cam tae yonder toon
   They bocht a loaf an they baith sat doon,
   They bocht a loaf an they baith sat doon,
   And the lassie ate wi her laddie.

8. And the lassie's courage began tae fail
   And her rosie cheeks grew wan and pale,
   And the tears came tricklin doun like hail
   Or a heavy shower in summer.

9. "Oh gin I were on yon high hill
   Whaur my father's flocks do feed their fill,
   I wad sit me doun an greet a while
   For the followin o my laddie."

10. When they cam tae yon marble gate
    Sae boldly as he knocked thereat,
    He rappit and he rappit late
    And he rappit there sae rudely.

11. Then four and twenty gentlemen
    Cam oot tae welcome the beggar hame,
    And just as many ladies gay
    Tae welcome the young knight's lady.

12. His brither John stood next the waa
    And he lauched till he wis like tae faa.
    "Oh brither, I wish we'd beggit aa
    For sic a bonny lassie."

13. "Yestreen I wis the beggar's bride,
    This nicht I'll lay doun by his side.
    I've come tae guid by my misguide,
    For noo I'm the young knight's lady."

5. Corachree

sung by Jimmy Hutchison, Newburgh

It hap-pened ae sim-mer eve-nin, I gaed oot tae tak___ the air And co-min in___ be Tar - land toon I met a love - ly___ pair. The youth was tall___ an hand-some and the___ maid___ fair tae see An I kent their des-ti- -na - tion___ wis-nae far___ frae Co-ra-chree.___

2. I stopped and watched their motions as they did pass me by.
   The sun was set, the nicht was fair; I heard what they did say.
   I drew my plaid aboot me and I set my cap agee
   And aa tae watch their motions comin in by Corachree.

3. Halfway up the avenue they baith sat doon tae rest.
   He put his airm aboot her crying, "Dear, I loe ye best.
   A maiden ye hae sitten doon and a maiden ye're aye tae me,
   But a maiden ye'll ne'er walk again throu the girse o Corachree."

4. "Oh Sandy lad, ye'll ne'er deny this thing that ye hae done.
   My apron strings are broken, Lord! my hair flees in the wind.
   My maidenheid has taen a fricht and flown awa fae me,
   And the Session Clerk will get tae ken o this thing ye've done tae me."

5. "Cheer up, ma bonny lassie, for ye needna get big;
   There's mony a bonny lassie that gangs daily on the rig.
   There's mony a bonny lassie ay, and just as guid as ye,
   But a maiden ye'll ne'er walk again through the girse o Corachree."

6. Noo he comes doon in the evening as often as he can;
   He comes doon in the evening just tae see his bonny Ann.
   They tak their len o auld lang syne whaur naebody can see,
   But ye'll easy find oot aa their beds neath the girse o Corachree.

12

6. The Bonny Hoose o Airlie

sung by Belle Stewart, Blairgowrie

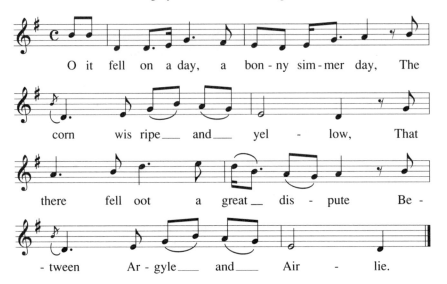

O it fell on a day, a bon-ny sim-mer day, The
corn wis ripe___ and___ yel - low, That
there fell oot a great ___ dis - pute Be -
- tween Ar - gyle___ and___ Air - lie.

2. Lady Margaret she stood on her high castle wall
   And oh, but she sighed sairly,
   Tae see Argyle and aa his men
   Come tae plunder the bonny hoose o Airlie.

3. "Come doon, come doon, Lady Margaret," he cried,
   "Come doon and kiss me fairly,
   Or I swear by mune and stars abune
   I'll no leave a standin stone in Airlie."

4. "I'll no come doon, ye fause Argyle,
   Nor will I kiss thee fairly.
   I widna kiss the fause Argyle
   Tho he widna leave a standin stone in Airlie.

5. "But if my guid lord had 'a been at hame
   As he's awa wi Chairlie,
   There widna come a Campbell frae Argyle
   Dare tread upon the bonny green o Airlie.

6. "For I hae borne him seven bonny sons -
   The eighth has never seen his daddy -
   And if I had as many owre again,
   They wad aa be men for Chairlie."

7. But poor Lady Margaret was forced tae come doon
   And oh, but she sighed sairly,
   For there in front o aa his men,
   She was ravished on the bowling green o Airlie.

8. Argyle in a rage he kinnlet sic a lowe,
   It rose tae the lift red and clearly,
   And poor Lady Margaret and aa her bairns
   Were smothered in the dark reek o Airlie.

9. "Draw your dirks, draw your dirks!" cried the brave Lochiel.
   "Unsheathe your sword!" cried Chairlie,
   "We'll kinnle sic a lowe roon the fause Argyle
   And licht it wi a spark oot o Airlie!"

7. Willie's Rare

sung by Annie Bell, Blairgowrie

O Wil - lie's rare and Wil - lie's fair And

Wil - lie's won - drous___ bon - ny, And Wil - lie hecht tae

mair - ry me Gin___ ere he mair - ried

o - ny Gin___ ere he mair - ried o - ny.___

2. But Willie's gaen whom I thocht on
   And does not hear me weepin.
   O spare a tear frae true-love's ee
   When other maids are sleepin,
   When other maids are sleepin.

3. O gentle wind that bloweth south
   From where my love repaireth,
   Carry a kiss from his sweet mouth
   And tell me how he fareth,
   And tell me how he fareth.

4. And tell sweet Willie tae come doon
   And hear the mavis singin,
   Tae see the birds on ilka bush
   And leaves aroon them hingin,
   And leaves aroon them hingin.

5. She socht him east, she socht him west,
   She socht him braid and narrow.
   Syne in the cliftin o a craig
   She's fund him droon'd in Yarrow,
   She's fund him droon'd in Yarrow.

8. Lord Randal

sung by Mabel Skelton, Arbroath

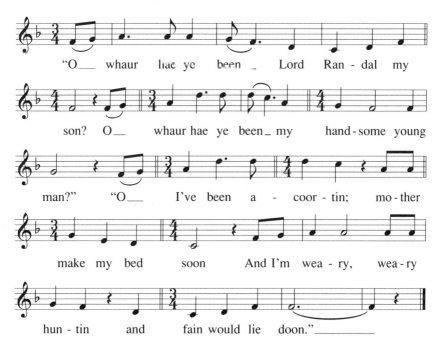

"O__ whaur hae ye been __ Lord Ran - dal my son? O__ whaur hae ye been_ my hand - some young man?" "O__ I've been a - coor - tin; mo - ther make my bed soon And I'm wea - ry, wea - ry hun - tin and fain would lie doon."_____

2. "What got ye to eat, Lord Randal my son?
   What got ye to eat, my little one?"
   "Eels, mother; mak my bed soon,
   For I'm sick tae the hairt and fain wad lie doon."

3. "What colour were those eels, Lord Randal my son?
   What colour were those eels, my little one?"
   "Green and speckled, mother; mak my bed soon,
   For I'm sick tae the hairt and fain wad lie doon."

4. "I fear ye are poisoned, Lord Randal my son,
   I fear ye are poisoned, my little one."
   "Yes, mother, I am poisoned; mak my bed soon,
   For I'm sick tae the hairt and fain wad lie doon."

9. Andra Lammie

sung by Jane Turriff, Mintlaw

At Mill o Tif - ty___ lived___ a man, In the
neigh - bour - hood_____ o Fy - vie. And he
had a love - ly___ daugh - ter fair, Her___
name was bon - ny___ An - nie.

2. Lord Fyvie had a trumpeter
   An his name was Andra Lammie
   And he had the art to win the heart
   O bonny Tifty's Annie.

3. Her mother called her to the door,
   "Come here tae me, my Annie.
   Did e'er you see a prettier man
   Than the trumpeter o Fyvie?"

4. Oh nothin she said but sighin sore,
   Alas for bonny Annie,
   But she durst not own that her heart was won
   By the trumpeter o Fyvie.

5. "O the first time me and my love did meet,
   It was in the woods o Fyvie,
   And he caaed me, 'Mistress.' I said, 'No,
   I am Tifty's bonny Annie.'

6. "With apples sweet he did me treat
   And kisses saft and many,
   And he had the art to gain the heart
   O bonny Tifty's Annie.

7. "O love comes in at my bedside
   And love lies doon beyond me,
   And love so oppressed my tender breast,
   O but love will waste my body.

8. " 'O lovey, I must go to Edinburgh toon
   And for a while I must leave ye.'
   'O but I'll be dead ere you come back,
   O bonny Andra Lammie.'

9. " 'O I will buy you a bridal gown
   And dearie, it will be bonny.'
   'O but I'll be dead ere you come back,
   O ma bonny Andra Lammie.'

10. "O love comes in at my bedside
    And love lies doon beyond me,
    And love so oppressed my tender breast,
    O but love will waste my body.

11. "O but lay me doon tae rest awhile
    And turn my face to Fyvie,
    That I may see before I dee
    O ma bonny Andra Lammie.

12. "O it's up and doon in Tifty's glen
    Whaur the burn lies clear and bonny,
    Whaur oft-times I have run tae thee,
    O ma bonny Andra Lammie.

13. "O love it dwines and love it twines
    And love decays my body,
    And love so oppressed my tender breast,
    O but love will waste my body."

14. O Andra hame fae Edinburgh came
    Wi muckle grief and sorrow,
    And he sounded his horn right loud and clear
    In the low lands o Fyvie.

15. "O Fyvie's lands are broad and wide
    And Fyvie's lands are bonny,
    Where oft-times I have gone to meet
    My bonny Tifty's Annie."

10. Hame Drunk Cam I

sung by Cameron Turriff, Fetterangus

When I cam hame on a Mon - day nicht,

hame drunk cam I, What did I spy in

my wife's bed but a pair o slip - pers did lie.

"O what is this you've got, pray what can it

be?" "It's a pair o floo - er - pots ma mi - ther sent tae

me." How ma - ny's a mile I've tra - velled, ten

thoo - san miles an more, It's a pair o floo - er - pots wi

soles on them I ne - ver saw be - fore!

2. When I cam hame on Tuesday nicht, hame drunk cam I,
   What did I spy in my wife's bed but a gentleman's vest did lie.
   "O what is this you've got, pray what can it be?"
   "It's a pair o steys ma mither sent tae me."
   How many's a mile I've travelled, ten thoosan miles an more,
   It's a dooble-breasted pair o steys I never saw before!

3. When I cam hame on Wednesday nicht, hame drunk cam I,
   What did I spy in my wife's bed but a gentleman's coat did lie.
   "O what is this you've got, pray what can it be?"
   "It's a petticoat ma mither sent tae me."
   How many's a mile I've travelled, ten thoosan miles an more,
   It's a petticoat wi a collar on't I never saw before!

4. When I cam hame on Thursday nicht, hame drunk cam I,
   What did I spy in my wife's bed but a pair o troosers did lie.
   "O what is this you've got, pray what can it be?"
   "It's a pair of bloomers ma mither sent tae me."
   How many's a mile I've travelled, ten thoosan miles an more,
   It's a pair o bloomers wi pooches in them I never saw before!

5. When I cam hame on Friday nicht, hame drunk cam I,
   What did I spy in my wife's bed but a gentleman's hat did lie.
   "O what is this you've got, pray what can it be?"
   "It's a chanty pot my mither sent tae me."
   How many's a mile I've travelled, ten thoosan miles an more,
   It's a chanty pot wi a riband on't I never saw before!

6. When I cam hame on Saturday nicht, hame drunk cam I,
   What did I spy in my wife's bed but a gentleman's face did lie.
   "O what is this you've got, pray what can it be?"
   "It's a new born babe ma mither sent tae me."
   How many's a mile I've travelled, ten thoosan miles an more,
   It's a new born babe wi whiskers on't I never saw before!

11. The Battle of Harlaw

sung by Jeannie Robertson, Aberdeen

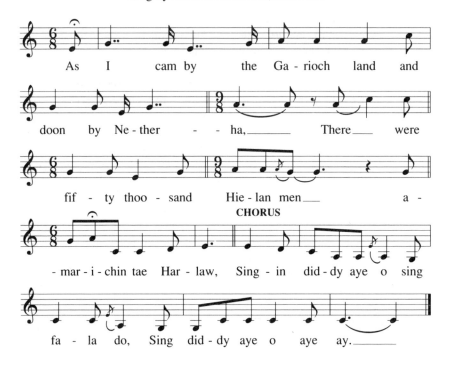

As I cam by the Ga - rioch land and doon by Ne - ther - - ha,_____ There____ were fif - ty thoo - sand Hie - lan men____ a - -mar - i - chin tae Har - law,

CHORUS

Sing - in did - dy aye o sing fa - la do, Sing did - dy aye o aye ay._____

2. "It's did ye come frae the Hielans, man, an did ye come aa the wye?
   An did ye see Macdonald and his men as they marched frae Skye?"

3. "For I've come frae the Hielans, man, an I've come aa the wye;
   An I saw Macdonald and his men as they marched frae Skye."

4. "An cam ye near an near eneuch, did ye their numbers see?
   Come tell tae me, John Hielanman, what might their numbers be?"

5. "For I was near an near eneuch an I their numbers saw;
   There were fifty thoosan Hielan men a-marchin tae Harlaw."

6. For they went on an further on an doon aboot Balquhine ;
   It's there they met Sir James the Rose, wi him Sir John the Graham.

7. "If that be so," said Sir James the Rose, "We'll no come muckle speed,
   We'll call upon oor merry men and we'll turn oor horses' heids."

8. "Oh nay, oh nay," said Sir John the Graham, "sic things we maunna dee.
   For the gallant Grahams were never beat and we'll try fit they can dee."

9. For they went on and further on and doon aboot Harlaw;
   The fell foe close on ilkae side, sic strikes ye never saw!

10. The fell foe close on ilkae side, sic strikes ye never saw,
    For ilkae sword gaed clash for clash at the battle o Harlaw.

11. The Hielanmen wi their lang swords fell doon on us fu sair,
    An they drove back oor merry men three acres breadth an mair.

12. Lord Forbes tae his brither did say, "Oh brither, dinna ye see,
    They've beat us back on ilkae side an we'll be forced tae flee."

13. "Oh nay, oh nay, my brither dear, oh nay that maunna be!
    For ye'll tak your guid sword in your hand an ye'll gang in wi me!"

14. For the twa brithers brave gaed in amang the thrang,
    An they smote doon the Hielanmen wi swords baith sharp and lang.

15. The first stroke Lord Forbes gied the brave Macdonald reeled,
    The neist stroke Lord Forbes gied the brave Macdonald fell.

16. What a cry amang the Hielanmen whan they saw their leader faa,
    They lifted him and buried him a lang mile frae Harlaw.

12. Alison Cross

sung by Lizzie Higgins, Aberdeen

Aal' A-li-son Cross she lives in yon tower, The ug-li-est witch in the north con-te-rie. His try-sted me ae day til her bower, An mo-ny a braw speech she's made tae me.

CHORUS A-wa a-wa ye ug-ly witch! Haud far a-wa an lat me be. A-fore I'll kiss yer ug-ly mou, I'll rai-ther tod-dle a-roon the tree.

2. She showed me a mantle o reid scarlet
   Wrocht wi gold and fringes fine.
   "Gin ye'll be my leman sae true,
   This guidly gift it sall be thine."

3. She showed me a sark o the saftest silk,
   Weel wrocht wi pearls abune the band.
   "Gin ye'll be my leman sae true,
   This guidly gift's at your command."

4. She showed me a cup o the guid reid gowd,
   Weel wrocht wi jewels sae fair and fine.
   "Gin ye'll be my leman sae true,
   This guidly gift it sall be thine."

5. She's taen oot her grass green horn;
   She blew it three times lood and shrill,
   Swore by the mune and stars abune
   She'd gar him rue the day he wis born.

6. She's taen oot her silver wand;
   She's turned three times aroon the tree,
   Muttered sic words that my senses failed
   And I fell doon senseless tae the ground.

7. Wi silver basin and silver kaim,
   Tae kaim ma heidie upon her knee.
   Aye on ilkae Saturday nicht
   Alison Cross she comes tae me.

8. It fell upon last Halloween,
   When the seely court cam ridin by.
   The Queen's lichtit doon on a gowan bank
   Nae far fae the tree whaur I did lie.

9. She's liftit me wi her milk white hand;
   She's straiked me three times on her knee,
   She's turned me back to my proper shape,
   Nae mair tae toddle aroon the tree.

Lizzie did not sing the chorus after every verse. Singers can make their own choice.

13. I Aince Hid a Lass

sung by Elizabeth Stewart, Mintlaw

I aince hid a lass,____ I__ li - kit her__ weel,____ I__ hate aa the peo - ple__ that__ spak o_____ her ill._____ But____ whit____ have I____ got - ten____ for_____ aa ma great lo - ve? She's____ a - wa tae be wed tae a - ni - ther._____

2. The next time I saw my love tae the church go,
   Wi bride and bridesmaidens they made a fine show,
   While I followed on wi a hert fu o woe,
   She's awa tae be wed tae anither.

3. The next time I saw my love in the church stand,
   Wi gold rings on her fingers and gloves in her hand,
   Wi gold rings on her fingers and gloves in her hand,
   She's gone tae be wed tae anither.

4. The minister that mairried them he gave a loud vow,
   "If there be any objection, then let him speak now."
   I thought in my ain hert objections had I
   For tae see ma love wed tae anither.

5. When mairriage wis owre an on intae dine,
   I fillt up the glasses wi brandy and wine.
   I leant owre the table tae kiss the sweet bride,
   Sayin, "She is the lassie that ought tae be mine."

6. When dinner wis owre an gaun intae bed,
   I put on ma hat an I bid them goodnight.
   The bridegroom said, "Stop or we speak jist a wee,
   Ye've whistled owre lang for tae get her."

7. "Ye can keep her an keep her an keep your great pride,
   For the bed that she lies in she canna deny.
   She has lain by my side, aince, twice and thrice,
   She's only my old shoes tho ye've got her."

8. O the folk o the forest they aa laugh at me,
   Sayin, "How many blaeberries growes in the saut sea?"
   I turnit richt roon wi a tear in my ee.
   "How many ships sail in the forest?"

9. Ye can dig me a grave an dig it sae deep,
   An I'll turn in for tae tak a lang sleep.
   An I'll turn in for tae tak a lang sleep
   An it's maybe throu time I'll forget her.

10. So they dug him a grave an they dug it sae deep,
    An he's turned in for tae tak a lang sleep.
    An he's turned in for tae tak a lang sleep,
    An it's maybe by noo he's forgotten.

14. Glenlogie

sung by Robert Lovie, New Aberdour

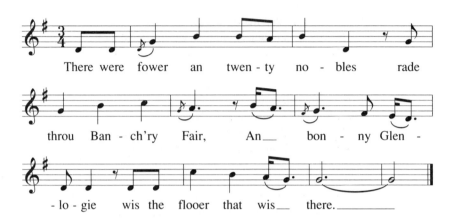

There were fower an twen-ty no-bles rade throu Ban-ch'ry Fair, An__ bon-ny Glen-lo-gie wis the flooer that wis__ there._____

2. There were nine and nine nobles sat at the king's dine
   An bonny Glenlogie was the flooer o twice nine.

3. Doon cam Jeannie Meldrum, she cam trippin doonstairs
   An she's chosen Glenlogie owre aa that wis there.

4. She called for his foot-boy who ran by his side,
   Sayin, "Wha is the young man an whaur does he bide?"

5. "His name is Glenlogie when he is at hame,
   But he's o the noble Gordons and his name is Lord John."

6. "Glenlogie, Glenlogie, gin ye'll prove kind,
   My love is laid on you, now I've told you my mind."

7. Noo Glenlogie turned lichtly as Gordons does aa,
   "I thank ye, Jeannie Meldrum, but I'm promised awa."

8. Then she called for her maidens tae mak her a bed,
   Wi ribbons and napkins tae tie up her head.

9. "Noo, lay me doon gently, my face tae the waa,
   Tak this rings fae my fingers, my jewels an aa."

10. Noo her faither's ain chaplin bein a man o great skeel,
    He's penned a braw letter an he's penned it richt weel.

11. When Logie read the letter, a licht lauch lauched he,
    But when he read the letter, the tears blint his ee.

12. "Gae saddle me the black horse, gae saddle me the grey!
    Bonny Jeannie o Bethelnie'll be deid ere I win."

13. Pale and wan wis she when Logie cam in,
    But reid and rosy grew she when she kent it wis him.

14. "Turn roon, Jeannie Meldrum, turn tae your richt side,
    For I'll be your bridegroom if ye'll be ma bride."

15. Noo Jeannie's got mairrit an her tocher's soon tauld,
    Bonny Jeannie o Bethelnie - scarce saxteen years auld.

16. Bethelnie, Bethelnie, ye shine whaur ye stand,
    May the heather bells roon ye shine owre Fyvie's land.

15. The Beggarman

sung by Robin Hutchison, Aberdeen

A beg-gar, a beg-gar cam owre yon lea, He was as-kin
lod - gins for cha-ri - ty. He was as-kin
lod-gins for cha-ri - ty, "Wad ye lodge a beg-gar-man?"

CHORUS

Lad-die lil-tie tow - row ray.

2. Wi the night bein dark an a wee bittie wat
   Doon tae the fireside the auld man sat.
   He castit the meal-pyocks aff his back
   An it's aye he rantit and sang.

3. O he widnae lie in stable, he widnae lie in byre,
   But he wid lie fore-anent the kitchen fire;
   O he wid lie fore-anent the kitchen fire,
   He's a gey auld beggarman.

4. When he got the auld folks asleep,
   Intae the daughter's bedroom he did creep;
   Intae the bedroom he did creep,
   He's a gey auld beggarman.

5. "Oh gin I wis black as I am white,
   Like snaw 't lies on thon fail-dyke,
   I wid dress masel as beggar like
   An awa wi you I'll gang."

6. "Oh lassie, oh lassie, ye're far too young,
   For ye hannae got the cant o the beggin tongue;
   Ye hannae got the cant o the beggin tongue
   An wi me ye canna gang."

7. "I'll bend ma back, I'll boo ma knee,
   I'll tie a black patch on ma ee,
   An for a beggar they'll tak me,
   An awa wi ye I'll gang."

8. This twa made up the plot,
   They'd rise twa oors before the auld cock.
   Sae gently did they slip the lock,
   An across the fields they've run.

9. Early in the morn when the auld folk rose,
   They missed the auld beggarman and his auld clothes;
   They missed the auld beggarman and his auld clothes,
   He's a gey auld beggarman.

10. "Gae awa ben auld wife and wauken the bairn,
    For the milk's tae kirn an the claes tae yirn."
    But the sheets wis cauld an she wis awa,
    She's awa wi the beggarman.

11. Oh they gaed tae the presses, they gaed tae the kist
    Tae see if ony guid gear wis missed;
    For tae see if ony o their guid gear wis missed,
    She's awa wi the beggarman.

12. Some gaed on horseback an some gaed on fit,
    But the auld woman she wisnae fit,
    She humplit aboot fae hip tae hip,
    He's a gey auld beggarman.

13. Seven lang years wis passed an gaen
Back came the same auld beggar again.
He wis askin lodgins for charity,
"Wid ye lodge a beggarman?"

14. "A beggar, a beggar I'll ne'er lodge again,
For I once had a daughter, only but ane,
An awa wi a beggarman she has gaen,
He's a gey auld beggarman."

15. "Oh auld wife, auld wife, whit wid ye gie
For ae sicht o yer daughter tae see;
For ae sicht o yer daughter tae see,
Gaed awa wi the beggarman."

16. "Oh ye wratch, ye wratch, if I thocht it wis you,
I wid mak ye hang wi the shafts o the ploo;
I wid mak ye hang wi the shafts o the ploo,
An I wish't I seen ye slain."

17. "Oh here she's comin owre thon lea,
Roarin oot yer charity,
Wi a bairn on her back an anither on her lap,
An ane on the road comin home."

18. "Here she's comin owre thon bower,
Ridin on her carriage an fower.
She holds up her hands an she blesses the hour
She follaed the beggarman."

16. Dumfries Hiring Fair

sung by Peter Fairbairn, Kilmarnock

I went tae Dum-fries Hi-ring Fair for tae get a

fee, An a-mang the ha-shy fair-mers ma

CHORUS

hairt's as licht's can be. Wi a mush-a-ma too-ra

lad-die o, An a mush-a-ma too-ra lay.

2. Auld Jock o the Dean comes owre tae me, says he, "Ye've had nae fair.
It's will ye come hame wi me tae drive ma second pair?

3. "If ye can haud the ploo a bit, an build a fair bit stack,
And at rising in the morning I hope ye'll no be slack."

4. Well, the horses that we got tae work they werena very braw,
Fur Jeanie she hud ae lame leg an Maggie she hud twa.

5. They kept a lassie aboot the place, the name o her was Jean,
The way the girl was treated was a god-almichty shame.

6. The milk that we got tae oor brose it wasna very new,
Fur it set the dugs a-howlin an it damn near killt the soo.

7. The scones they were blue mouldit, the kale it hud a smell,
Ay, an even in the winter time the beef could run itsel.

8. The auld gude wife at dennertime sat up at the table heid,
Begrudgin every bit we ett an wishin we were deid.

9. But term time's comin roon again an I dinna gie a hang,
Fur I'll pack up ma auld duddies an I'll gang the road I cam.

17. The Diamond Jubilee

sung by Dick Cowan, New Castleton

For I'm jist a sim-ple Scotch-man, a can-ny so-ber chiel, But

mind I ken ma way a-boot, I ken it braw an weel. For I'm

jist new doon fae Lon-don toon, wi' yon place I a-gree, I

went up there to ce-le-brate the Dia-mond Ju-bi-

CHORUS

- lee. For I'm jist new doon fae Lon-don toon,

See - in the Queen in her gol - den croon,

Aa the folk fae roon an roon_____ Were

sta-rin ef-ter me. For they liked me style, they liked me smile, They

took me for the Duke o Ar-gyle, By jin-go I did go my mile, At the

Dia - mond Ju - bi - lee.

2. Now on the celebration day it was a sight to see:
   The folk were there in millions and most o them knew me.
   Me neck was stiff wi noddin at the folk there to be seen,
   And the first yin there tae nod tae me was oor ain guid gracious Queen.

3. Now after the celebration to the palace we retired,
   Noblemen, common men, all splendidly attired.
   The moment that I entered they all set up a cheer,
   Don't be surprised if some day soon the Queen makes me a peer.

18. The Packman

sung by Dave McFadzean, Thornhill

I'm a puir shep-herd lad-die and Mur-ray by name,_____ Tae be a Scots pack-man tae Grims-by I came._____ I left my auld fai-ther___ an mi-ther an aw._____ Ma leal___ hair-ted cro-nies___ in wild___ Gal - lo-wa.___

2. The nicht that I landed I gaed doon the street
An jist in the bull-ring the boss I did meet.
He glowered in ma face and held oot his paw,
Sayin, "Are ye ma laddie fae wild Gallowa?"

3. He then took me in an he tret me richt weel,
But wae aw his kindness fae hame I did feel.
An o fine English feedin I soon taen a staw,
An I sighed for the meal brose in wild Gallowa.

4. Weel I was next mornin rigged oot wi a pack,
   An sent off a-whiskin some orders tae tak.
   But I soon fun that whiskin wid no dae at aw,
   An I wished I was safe back in wild Gallowa.

5. For I met wi refusals in maisten ilk place,
   They shook their heids at me, slammed doors in ma face.
   An some let their dugs oot tae fricht me awa,
   Insultin the laddie fae wild Gallowa.

6. Some orders I took that he coudna supply,
   An when we next met they wid ask tae ken why.
   They cawed me a lazy Scots swindler an aw -
   Ill-used the puir laddie fae wild Gallowa.

7. Sae since I'm a failure tae this loopy trade,
   I'll gae back tae fair Scotland and redd on ma plaid.
   An I'll roam wi ma dug mang the heather sae braw,
   An I'll snuff the fresh breezes o wild Gallowa.

8. So aw ye young lads that wid gang tae the pack,
   Frae yin that's been there this advice ye maun tak;
   At plooin and herdin tho puirer ye faw,
   Ye'll find mair contentment in wild Gallowa.

19. I Must Away, Love

sung by Bobby Robb, Girvan

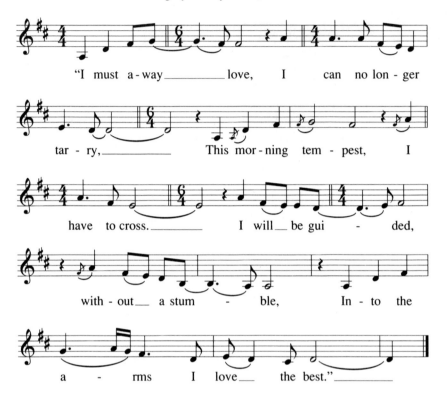

"I must a-way_____ love, I can no lon-ger tar - ry,_____ This mor-ning tem - pest, I have to cross._____ I will_ be gui - ded, with - out_ a stum - ble, In - to the a - rms I love_ the best."_____

2. An when he came to his true love's dwelling,
   He knelt him gently upon a stone,
   An through the window he whispered lowly,
   "Is my true love within, at home?"

3. She's raised her up from her down-soft pillow,
   She's weaved a blanket aroond her breast,
   Sayin, "Wha is that at my bedroom window,
   Disturbing me at my night's rest?"

4. "Wake up, wake up, love, it is your own true lover,
   Wake up, wake up, love, and let me in!
   For I am wet, love, and oh sae weary,
   For I am wet, love, untae my skin."

5. She's raised her up wi the greatest o pleasure,
   She's raised her up and let him in.
   They baith shook hands and embraced each other,
   Until the mornin they lay as yin.

6. And when the long night was past and over,
   And when the sma clouds began to grow,
   They've embraced, ay, they've kissed and parted,
   He's saddled and mounted and away did go.

   (Repeat first verse)

20. Burke and Hare

sung by Angus Russell, Kilwinning

For the help o folk in Me-di-cal School the
word is pit a-roon,_____ That a
bo-dy__ nae mair nor ten days cold can
fetch ye a guid ten pound. O sad it is but
true to say in our wic-ked__ warld o greed,__ A
man's worth no-thing when a-live but plen-ty when he's

CHORUS

deid. They went up the close an doon the stair, A
but an ben wi Burke an Hare. Burke's the but-cher,
Hare's the thief, Knox is the man wha buys the beef.

2. So in the dark o mony a nicht when aw guid folk are sleepin,
   Alang the dyke and through the kirk-yaird there cam twa shadows creepin.
   And mony a corpse that's stark and cauld and safely laid away
   Ne'er thinkin it wis no the last it had seen the licht o day.

3. But no content wi howkin deid - a ploy that aye gets harder -
   They cast their een on livin folk an start committin murder.
   But Reekie toon can sleep at last, the twa sall hunt nae mair -
   It's the gallows tree for William Burke and a pauper's grave for Hare.

21. Bonny Laddie Ye Gang By Me

sung by Heather Heywood, Kilmarnock

It__ hap-pened on a day_____ in the
mer-ry month o May,_____ I gaed
oot tae meet__ ma bon-ny lad, he
pro-mised tae come__ ma way_____ I gaed
oot tae meet__ ma bon-ny lad,__ he
pro-mised tae come ma way, But ma
bon-ny lad-die ne-ver yet cam by me.__

2. "O whit hae I said, love, and whit hae I done,
And whit objections tae me hae ye found?
Or hae ye gaen a-coortin anither pretty maid;
Is that the reason, laddie, ye gang by me ?"

3. "O naethin hae ye said, love, an naethin hae ye done,
   And nae objection tae ye hae I found,
   But I hae gaen a-coortin another pretty maid,
   Aye and that's the reason, lassie, I gang by ye."

4. "O ye micht hae coortit six and ye micht hae coortit seiven,
   Ye micht hae coortit echt, nine, ten and eleiven;
   Ye micht hae coortit dozens aw owre an owre again,
   But been kinder tae your auld love for aw that.

5. "O the hills they are high and the leaves they are green,
   And mony is the happy nicht that you and I hae seen,
   But there's anither lassie a-dancin in ma sheen
   And sae neatly, bonny laddie, ye gang by me.

6. "O the hills they are high but the leaves arenae rotten,
   Although ma love has left me, I'm no hert-broken.
   For I'll coort anither lad and you'll soon be forgotten,
   Then sae neatly, bonny laddie, I'll gang by ye."

42

22. The Weaver's Lamentation

sung by Adam Macnaughtan, Glasgow

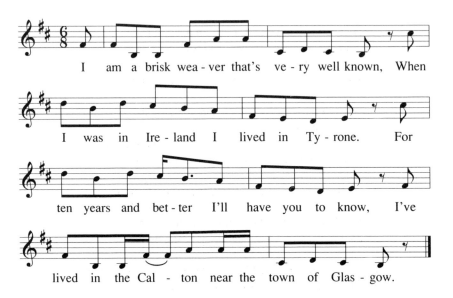

I am a brisk wea-ver that's ve-ry well known, When
I was in Ire-land I lived in Ty-rone. For
ten years and bet-ter I'll have you to know, I've
lived in the Cal - ton near the town of Glas-gow.

2. The first five years when the trade it was good,
   We never went short either for claes or food.
   I'd plenty of credit wherever I'd caw
   But now trade is down, there's no credit at aw.

3. My loom bein idle and the mills on half time,
   I and my family began to decline,
   And hundreds o tradesmen as ill-off as I
   A peck o potatoes or meal couldnae buy.

4. So we aw did assemble one day on the Green,
   For no bad intention it's plain to be seen.
   'Twas simply to let aw the gentlefolk know
   That the want o work was the cause o our woe.

5. Then with circumspection reviewing our case,
   They said, "It's a pity to see in this place
   So many going idle, and good tradesmen too,
   That's willing to work if they had it to do."

6. They allowed to the quarry we all should repair,
   And them that were married they'd find them work there.
   We thank them sincerely; what could we do less?
   For many the faimily they've saved frae distress.

7. 'Twas on Monday morning we all marched away,
   The third of April, I'll aye mind that day.
   With our hammers in hand and green aprons also
   In full uniform to work we did go.

8. When first I began at the knappin o stanes,
   I quit every night wi cut hands and sair banes.
   I no bein accustomed to work oot o doors,
   It didnae agree wi me, you may be sure.

9. When first I began the whinstanes for to break,
   Five shillings a week was the maist I could make.
   I'll allow there were others that made above nine,
   But their hands nor their backs werenae sair as mine.

10. I wrocht for nine days till my back grew that sair,
    I had to gie up for I could knap nae mair.
    To my old employer my case I made known,
    But he told me his case was as bad as my own.

11. But I have good news now for my countrymen:
    One shilling will take them back home in "The Finn."
    If I were in Ireland, no more I would roam
    For in good times or bad there is no place like home.

12. Goodbye to the Calton and Brigton also,
    And the lads and the lasses back there in Glasgow.
    I'll never forget while blood runs in my veins,
    The nine days I spent at the knappin o stanes.

23. Tattie Jock

sung by Davey Stewart, Glenrothes

Ye aa hae heard o— Tat - tie Jock, like - wise o Mut - ton Peg - gy. They kept a ferm in the north o Fife, an the name o— it wis Crai - gie.

CHORUS

Hi rid - dle di, roo rum ri— do, Hi rid - dle di,— roo—rum day.

2. Three months we served wi Tattie Jock an weel we did agree,
   When we fund oot that the tattie shed could be opened wi the bothy key.

3. Next mornin in the tattie shed, oor bags were hardly full,
   When Tattie Jock in ahint the door cries, "Aa ma lads, staun still!"

4. Noo the first he got wis Willie Marr, the next wis Sandy Doo,
   There wis Jimmy Gray an Will Moncur an Jimmy Pethrie flew.

5. They sent for ten big polismen, but nine there only cam,
   It dinged them fur tae lift us that night, us bein ten able men.

6. Noo the youngest lad wis the wisest lad, the best lad o us aa,
   He jined a man-o-war at Leith so he neednae staund the law.

7. As we were gettin wir sentences we aa stood roon an roon,
   But when we heard o the thirteen years, ach the tears cam a-tricklin doon.

8. As we were bein mairched up throu Perth, I heard the newsboy say,
   "It's sad tae see sic able men rade off tae Botany Bay".

9. And when we get tae Botany Bay, some letters we will send,
   Tae tell oor friends o the hardships we endure in a foreign land.

24. The Collier Laddie

sung by Irene Riggs, Kirkcaldy

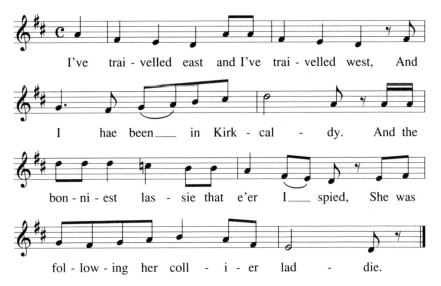

I've trai-velled east and I've trai-velled west, And
I hae been___ in Kirk - cal - dy. And the
bon-ni-est las - sie that e'er I___ spied, She was
fol-low-ing her coll - i - er lad - die.

2. "Oh whaur live ye, my bonny lass?
   Come tell me whit they caa ye."
   "Oh bonny Jean Gordon is ma name
   And I'm followin ma collier laddie."

3. "Oh see ye not yon hills and dales
   The sun shines on sae brawly?
   Well they're aa mine and shall be thine,
   Gin ye'll leave yer collier laddie.

4. "And ye shall gang in gay attire,
   Weel buskit up sae brawly,
   Wi ane tae wait on every hand,
   If ye'll leave yer collier laddie."

5. "Well I winna hae yer lands and I winna hae yer rents,
   Ye'll never mak me a lady,
   For I'd raither gae wi yin that's black
   Than you wi aa yer money.

6. "O love for love is the bargain for me,
   Tho a wee cot hoose should haud me,
   And I'll mak ma bed in a collier's neuk,
   And lie doon wi ma collier laddie."

25. Macpherson's Rant

sung by Davie Stewart, Aberdeen

Fare ye weel, ye dark and__ lone - ly hills, Fare -
weel be - neath__ the sky._____ Mac -
- pher - son's rant will__ nae be lang Be -
- low the gal - lows tree. O ran - tin - ree, ran - tin - ree__

CHORUS

Ran - tin ree__ was he. He played a tune an he
danced it roon Be - low the gal - lows tree.

2. It was low aneath her window sole
   A blanket she threw over me,
   Tae plead the cause o Jimmy Broon
   An set Macpherson free.

3. 'Twas the Laird o Grant, that Hieland sant
   That first laid hands on me,
   Tried the cause o Jimmy Broon
   And he let Macpherson free.

4. "Fareweel, ma ain dear Heilan hame,
   Fareweel, ma wife an bairns.
   There was nae repentance in my hairt
   When ma fiddle was in ma airms."

5. The reprieve was comin owre the Brig o Banff
   When I stood on the Gallows Hill to see.
   They put the clock three quarters fast
   An marched him to the tree.

6. "Fareweel, fareweel, Macpherson dear,
   The day's come that ye maun dee."
   "But God'll protect ma wife an bairns
   When I swing below the tree.

7. "A fig now for the English law
   That first condemned me.
   Fareweel, auld Scotland, there I'll dee,
   I'll swing below the tree.

8. "Many come here tae buy ma fiddle,
   And mair come here tae see me dee,
   But afore I will sell my fiddle
   I'll brak her across my knee."

26. The Donibristle Mossmorran Disaster

sung by John Watt, Milnathort

On the twen - ty sixth of Au - gust our
fa - tal moss gave way, Al - though we did our
le - vel best___ its course we could not stay. Ten
pre - cious lives there were at stake "Who'll
save them?" was the cry, "We'll bring them to the
sur - face or a - long with them we'll die."

2. There was Rattray and McDonald, Hynd and Patterson,
   Too well they knew the danger and the risk they had to run.
   They never stopped to count the cost, "We'll save them!" was the cry,
   "We'll bring them to the surface or along with them we'll die."

3. They stepped upon the cage, they were ready for the fray,
   We knew they all meant business as they chapped themselves away.
   They quickly reached the bottom far from the light of day,
   They were off to search the workings and Tom Rattray led the way.

4. They lost their lives, God help them, oh yes, it was a fact,
   Someone put a stopping, so of course, they ne'er got back.
   Was that another blunder ? My God, it was a sin !
   To put that cruel stopping for it closed our heroes in.

5. But we never shall forget them, nor how they lost their lives,
   So we must pay attention to their children and their wives.
   It simply is our duty, so let us all beware,
   Their fathers died a noble death and left them in our care.

50

27. The Porter Laddie

sung by Jock Lundie, Auchtermuchty (formerly Perthshire)

Far owre yon__ hill there lives__ a las - sie,__
And her name I__ do__ not know, This
ve - ry__ night I will go and__ see__ her__
Whe - ther__ she be__ high__ or low.

2. This very night I'll go and see her
Though not a star shines from above.
I will be guided without a stumble
Right into the arms of my own true love.

3. As I reached my true love's window
I kneeled down gently upon a stone.
A pane bein broken in the window,
Says I, "Fair maid, do you lie alone?"

4. She raised her head from her snow-white pillow,
She raised her hands from her lily-white breast,
Sayin, "Who is this at my bedroom window
Disturbin me from my quiet night's rest?"

© The Hardie Press 1995

5. "'Tis I, 'tis I, your own true love.
   Open the door and let me in.
   This very night I hae come tae see ye,
   Besides I am soakin tae the skin."

6. She opened the door wi the greatest pleasure,
   She opened and she let me in.
   We both clasped hands and embraced each other,
   And all that night we lay as yin.

7. The cocks are crowin, the birds are whistlin,
   The burns they run high abune the brae,
   And I am just a puir plooman laddie
   And the fairmer I must obey.

8. "Oh now, my love, I must go and leave you,
   Tae climb the hills that are far above.
   But I will climb wi the greatest o pleasure,
   Since I've been in the arms o my ain true love."

28. Hatton Woods

sung by Cathy Higgins, Blairgowrie

Kind___ com-rades an com-pan-ions, and
all ye fe-males dear, To my sad la-men-
-ta-tion,___ I'll___ pray you lend___ an
ear. For once I loed___ a bon-ny lass___ an to
me she___proved un-true, And I left her doon___ by
Hat-ton wids___ my fol-ly for tae rue.

2. I courted wi this bonny lass a twelvemonth an a day,
   Sometimes among the green grass, sometimes among the hay.
   I courted her the lee-lang nicht and part o the next day,
   Till she said, "My dearest Sandy lad, it's time you were away."

3. I said, "My dearest Molly lass, when will we set a time
   When you an I'll get married an hands together jine?
   Ye'll sit in yon wee cottar hoose an either spin or shew
   While your ain guid-hairted Sandy lad goes whistlin at the ploo."

4. Noo there's Caddam and there's Caddam Mill and Lowthrie Mills likewise,
   There's woods an waters many unseen unto our eyes,
   But the bonny woods o Hatton, they aye grow green in May
   An there the bonny lassie dwells wha stole my hairt away.

5. My blessing on yon bonny lass, wherever she may be.
   I think no evil unto her, altho she slighted me.
   I only wish that she may say someday afore I dee,
   "I wish I'd wed yon plooman lad wha sang sae sweet tae me."

29. Jamie Foyers

sung by Willie MacPhee, Perthshire

Far a dis - tance, far a
dis - tance lies Sco - tia___ the brave, No
tomb - stone___ or___ me - mo - rial to
hal - low___ his___ grave.___ His bones they lie___
scat - tered on the rude soil o Spain, where
young Ja - mie Foy - ers in bat - tle was slain.

2. To the Perthshire Militia to serve in the line,
   The brave Forty Second bound for to join,
   To storm Burgos Castle before the break o day
   Along with bold Foyers, a young Iron Grey.

3. But by climbin the ladder and scalin the wall
   A bullet from a French gun young Foyers did fall.
   He leaned his right arm upon his left breast
   And fell from the ladder, putting off his request.

4. "To you, Robert Peerie, who stands the campaign,
   If goodness should send you to Scotland again,
   You can tell my old mother, as long may she mourn,
   That her son, Jamie Foyers, will never return.

5. "But if I had one drink of Baker's Brown Well,
   My thirst it would quench an my drouth it would quell.
   You can tell my old father, if yet his heart warms,
   That his son, Jamie Foyers, expired in your arms."

6. Oh the bugles may sound and the war drums may rattle,
   Nae mair will this hero to war or to battle,
   For he fell from the ladder like a soldier so brave,
   And young Jamie Foyers lies in his cold grave.

30. The Magdalen Green

sung by Jim Reid, Dundee

"O___ here I am a___ stran - ger, just

new come frae the sea,___ My ship she lies at an -

- chor___ in the har - bour___ o___ Dun -

- dee. Your face it is the fai - rest that

e - ver___ I___ hae seen. O___ fair maid, wad ye___

walk wi me doon by the Magda - len Green.

2. A roguish smile upon her face, she answered me and said,
   "Kind Sir, I'd go along with you but you know I am afraid.
   The paths they are so slippery, the night so cold and keen.
   It would not do for me to fall doon by the Magdalen Green."

3. With kind words and promises along with me she went.
   We rambled here, we rambled there, on love and pleasure bent.
   Day after day we met and roved about that pleasant scene -
   I fear the maid had many a fall doon by the Magdalen Green.

4. But soon the time for parting came, my ship had hoisted sail.
   No longer could I see my dear, to tell love's pleasant tale.
   We sang farewell to old Dundee, where I had happy been,
   And she was left to walk alone doon by the Magdalen Green.

5. As I lay in my berth one night when my weary watch was done,
   I dreamt I was the father of a darling little son.
   And in my dream his mother, too, right plainly she was seen,
   And she was weeping bitterly doon by the Magdalen Green.

6. O when my ship puts in again at the harbour of Dundee,
   I'll search the town all up and down until my girl I see.
   I'll ask her to forgive me, for the rascal I have been,
   And we will make it up again doon by the Magdalen Green.

7. Come all ye jolly sailors bold, a warning take by me,
   And never slight a poor girl for all her poverty.
   To lightly love and sail away is neither straight nor clean,
   So never do as I once did doon by the Magdalen Green.

58

31. Jamie Raeburn

sung by Willie Barclay, Perthshire

O my name is Ja - mie Rae - burn, in Glas - gow I was born, My place and ha - bi - ta - tion I'm forced to leave in scorn. From my place and ha - bi - ta - tion I noo maun gang a - wa, Far frae the bon - ny hills an dales o Ca - le - do - ni - a.

2. It was early one Monday mornin jist aboot the break o day,
When I overheard the turnkey these words to us did say,
"Arise you helpless convicts, arise ye one an aa,
For this is the day you're gaun tae stray fae Caledonia."

3. It's fareweel, my aged mother, I'm vexed for what I've done,
And I hope they'll never upcast you the race that I hae run.
And I hope you'll be provided fur when I am far awa,
Far fae the bonny hills and dales o Caledonia.

4. Fareweel, my aged father, ye are the best o men.
   Fareweel tae you, my darlin love, young Catherine's her name.
   It's no more we'll rove by Clyde's clear streams or by the Broomielaw,
   O fare ye weel ye hills and dales ioon Caledonia.

5. I hope the next place we shall meet that it shall be above,
   Where hallelujahs shall be sung by He who rules in love.
   No earthly judge to judge us there, but He who judges aa.
   Fareweel, ye bonny hills and dales o Caledonia.

32. The Banks o Inverurie

sung by Andy Stirling, Carrbridge

One_ day as I was walk - ing and
doon as I did pass,_____ On the banks of In - ve -
- ru - rie I spied a bon - ny lass. Her
hair hung o'er__ her shoul - ders, and her
eyes like dia - monds fair shine, On the Banks of In - ve -
- ru - rie and o gin she were mine!

2. I did embrace this fair maid as fast as e'er I could;
   Her hair hung o'er her shoulders fair all in its threads of gold.
   Her hair hung o'er her shoulders fair and her eyes like drops of dew -
   "On the banks of Inverurie, I long to walk with you."

3. She said, "Young man, give over, do not delude me so,
   For after kissing cometh wooing and after wooing, woe.
   My tender heart you would ensnare and I'd beguiled be,
   On the banks of Inverurie, were I to walk with thee."

4. She said, "Young man, give over, my company refrain,
   I know you are of gentle blood, but of a graceless clan.
   I know your occupation, lad, and good you cannot be,
   On the banks of Inverurie, I'll walk alone," said she.

5. I said, "My pretty fair maid, the truth I'll ne'er deny.
   On the banks of Inverurie, twelve maids beguiled have I.
   I used to flatter fair maids, but now it shall not be,
   On the banks of Inverurie, if you will walk with me."

6. He put a horn to his lips and blew both loud and shrill,
   Till six and thirty armed men came to their master's call.
   He said, "I used to flatter maids, but now it shall not be,
   On the banks of Inverurie, my wedded wife you'll be.

7. "So come, my pretty fair maid, and mount on horseback high,
   And we will to the parson go, and that immediately.
   And I will sing those lines with joy until the day I dee,
   In praise of Inverurie's banks, where first I met with thee."

33. Roy's Wife o Aldivalloch

sung by Stanley Robertson, Aberdeen

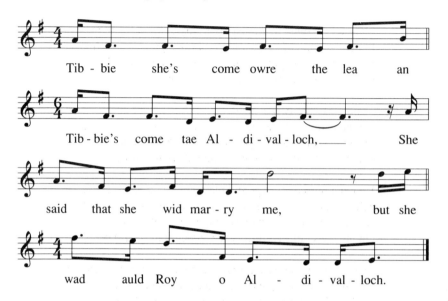

Tib - bie she's come owre the lea an

Tib - bie's come tae Al - di - val - loch,_____ She

said that she wid mar - ry me, but she

wad auld Roy o Al - di - val - loch.

CHORUS*

   Roy's wife o Aldivalloch, Roy's wife o Aldivalloch,
   O sae hoo she diddled me as I came owre the braes o Balloch.

2. She swore, she vowed she wad be mine, and loue me abeen ony,
   But o the fickle, faithless quine, she's taen the gee and left her Johnnie.

3. O she wis a highland queen, and she could dance the hielan walloch.
   O if only she were mine, or I auld Roy o Aldivalloch.

4. Her hair sae fair, her eye sae clear, her wee bit mou sae sweet and bonny,
   But oh, she's up and left me here, and she's forever left her Johnnie.

5. But Roy's thrice aulder man than I, perhaps his days will no be mony,
   And whin the carle is deid and gone, then she'll come hame tae her Johnnie.

6. Tibbie she's came owre the lea, and Tibbie's came tae Aldivalloch,
   She said that she wid mairry me, but she's wad auld Roy o Aldivalloch.

   * CHORUS repeats complete melody

34. The P D Drifters

sung by Frank Duthie, Findochty

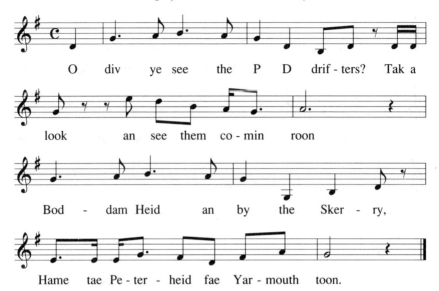

O div ye see the P D drif - ters? Tak a

look an see them co - min roon

Bod - dam Heid an by the Sker - ry,

Hame tae Pe - ter - heid fae Yar - mouth toon.

2. On every caff sack in their caibins
   There's a baggie bairns are waitin for at hame,
   Stappit full o rock an sweeties,
   Nuts an every galshach ye could name.

3. For granny there's a bonny pentit platie or a dishie,
   She kens she aye gets ane every year,
   "A present fae Great Yarmouth" will be written roon aboot it
   So far it's come fae naeb'dy needs tae speir.

4. Mither she is bound tae get a pair o carpets,
   The pair she has ere noo are wearin deen.
   She's hardly had them off sin the day that she got them,
   Her taes are aye sair grippit fae her sheen.

5. So div ye see the P.D. Drifters?
   Ye can see their smokin funnels comin roon.
   Fit say we aa rise up an rin doon tae the cannon
   An bid them welcome hame fae Yarmouth toon?

35. Brose Aa Day

sung by Jock Weatherston, Dalmeny

I was on-ly a half-lin when I left the glen, Tae

work as an or-ra-man doon at Kil-glen. It was

fair-ly a change for a lad-die like me, Tae get

brose for ma break-fast, ma den-ner and tea.

2. Noo brose in the mornin is aa verra weel,
   For they dinna need chowin wi the mulk ye can sweel.
   But as dennertime cam, losh, I'd rather haen bree
   Than brose tae ma breakfast, ma denner an tea.

3. At the ploo, I have often made picters o meat
   An winnered hoo lang on the brose they wad keep's.
   But when dennertime cam, wi a tear in ma ee,
   I gaed in tae the brose for ma denner an tea.

4. On the lang simmer's nights when castin the peats,
   I was often that famished I could have eaten ma beets.
   I nibbled on carrots, I'll no tell a lee,
   For it's a lang time on brose tween your denner an tea.

5. Noo that is the wye that I fell in wi Jean,
   She wis kitchie at Hilly's an just turned sixteen.
   She taen peety an whilies a cookie she'd gie's,
   'Twas a cheenge frae the brose tae yer denner an tea.

6. Noo that is the wye in the life o a man,
   Jist tae feed the breet up aye the best that we can.
   Jeannie thocht o't herself but she said she'd agree
   Tae gie me brose for ma breakfast, but no for ma tea.

7. They say folk hae thriven on hoddan an hose,
   An they say there's nae maik o a bowlfu o brose.
   I dinnae misdoot it but whit aboot three
   Bowles o brose for your breakfast, your denner an tea?

36. Eence Upon a Time

sung by Ray Fisher, Whitley Bay

2. My mistress aft-times said tae me and weel I ken she's richt O,
   That I maun be safe in the hoose afore twas candlelicht O.

3. But Johnny took me for his ain and I wis weel contentit,
   Noo these nights are past and gaen, it's aft-times I've repentit.

4. For Johnny he is lang since gaen and thinks o me nae mair O,
   And I maun seek anither lad tae faither Johnny's bairn O.

5. But dinna ye think, ma bonny lad, that I am mad aboot ye,
   For I can dae wi a lad and I can dae withoot ye.

6. So lassies aa tak heed o me when the threshin time it faas O,
   Be sure ye gaither in the grain and no the chaff that blaws O.

37. New Ferm Toon

sung by Eck Harley, Cupar, Fife

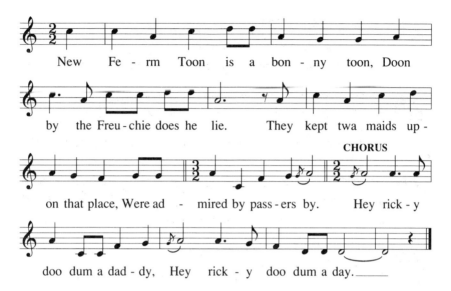

New Fe - rm Toon is a bon - ny toon, Doon
by the Freu - chie does he lie. They kept twa maids up -
on that place, Were ad - mired by pass - ers by. Hey rick - y
doo dum a dad - dy, Hey rick - y doo dum a day._____

2. The foreman upon that place,
   He thought he could tak the lead.
   It's true what Grannie Glover said,
   There's a saft bit in his heid.

3. The second man upon that place,
   He drove a pair o dashy broons,
   An when he got them on the road
   Try an follow them if ye can.

4. The third man upon that place,
   He was little years ava,
   But he sneaked up to the kitchen door
   An got the kirn to caa.

5. The fourth man upon that place,
   He thought himsel nae mock,
   But when he went doon the Netherburn
   He got puddens in a poke.

6. The cattleman upon the place,
   He was fine for feeding beef,
   But Deil the little could he eat
   For he's lossin aa his teeth.

7. There were three women workers upon the place,
   Their names I winna tell.
   For cursin an for sweirin
   They'll ne'er pass the gates o Hell.

38. Macfarlane o the Sprots

sung by 'Collessie' Kate Halliday, Lenzie

A - fore that I'd be ty - ran - eesed as I this file hae been, I'd

rai - ther walk fae here tae Birse wi peas in baith ma sheen; I'd

rai - ther dee for want o breath than pine for want o love, And it's

aa be - cause Mac - far - lane mair - rit Su - sie.

Su - sie's can - kert fai - ther wi mine could ne - ver gree, An

aye fin I gaed owre that gait he'd sen his dog at me. I

sent ma freen Mac - far - lane doon tae try fat he could dee; Mac-

far - lane o the Sprots o Bir - nie - boo - sie.

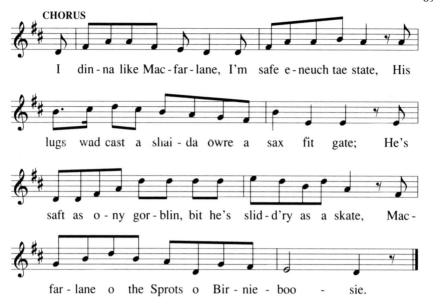

CHORUS

I din-na like Mac-far-lane, I'm safe e-neuch tae state, His lugs wad cast a shai-da owre a sax fit gate; He's saft as o-ny gor-blin, bit he's slid-d'ry as a skate, Mac-far-lane o the Sprots o Bir-nie-boo - sie.

2. Macfarlane spak nae word for me bit plenty for himsel.
   He reest the lassie's barley scones, her kebbuck and her kale.
   Her faither cried oot, "Sprots, ye shid try yer luck yersel!"
   Tae Macfarlane o the Sprots o Birnieboosie.
   Macfarlane he's the grimmest chiel for twenty mile aa roon,
   They buy his fottygraf tae fleg the rottans fae the toon.
   He's kittlet up his spunk at this, an speirt gin she'd come doon
   An be mistress o the Sprots o Birnieboosie.

   CHORUS
   I dinna like Macfarlane, I'll tell ye it's a fack;
   He's a nase for splittin hailstanes an a humphy back,
   Legs like gutta percha, ilka step his knees gyang knack,
   Macfarlane o the Sprots o Birnieboosie.

(continues over page)

3. He said that he was able tae play at cowp-the-ladle
   Wi a ledder owre a treacle cask an caa the churn forby.
   Anither o his winners wis that sawdust mixed wi cinners
   Wis their spice for feedin hens at Birnieboosie.
   An educatit ostrich fae the wilds o Timbuctoo
   They had for scartin up their neeps an hadna them tae pu;
   I never heard the like o that come oot o ony mou
   Bit Macfarlane o the Sprots o Birnieboosie.

   CHORUS
   I dinna like Macfarlane, it's awfy bit it's true.
   A pewter spune wis tint in Jock Macfarlane's mou,
   He couldna weel be grimmer an they feed him wi a skimmer,
   Macfarlane o the Sprots o Birnieboosie.

4. O a dirl o the teethache's nae particularly sweet,
   Bit love's the only pain on earth that ever gart me greet.
   It's like kittly chilblains roon yer hert, instead o roon yer feet;
   They were aggravatit by the sicht o Susie.
   Noo freens and kind philosophers, ye've heard fat me befell;
   Never lippen tae a middleman, bit dee yer wark yersel,
   Or I'll bet ma winter sark it's ye're a day ahint the market,
   Like fin I sent Macfarlane doon tae Susie.

   CHORUS
   I dinna like Macfarlane, I'm fairly aff o Jock.
   I dinna like Macfarlane or Macfarlane's folk.
   May his Susie be nae turtle bit the tangs aran the spurtle,
   Bring owre the heid o Jock o Birnieboosie.

39. The Braes o Bonald

sung by Tom Webster, Kinross

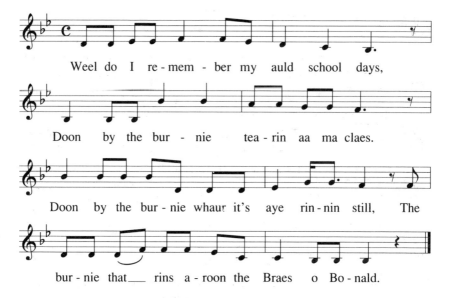

Weel do I re-mem-ber my auld school days,

Doon by the bur-nie tea-rin aa ma claes.

Doon by the bur-nie whaur it's aye rin-nin still, The

bur-nie that___ rins a-roon the Braes o Bo-nald.

CHORUS*
The Braes o Bonald, they're aye clad wi weans,
Some are pu'in daisies and ithers flingin stanes.
When the cuckoo's callin tae the sheep upon the hill,
It maks me contented on the Braes o Bonald.

2. Noo if you hae a bonny lass, I'll tell ye where tae gang:
   Gang for a ramble and as you stroll along,
   Just ask her for tae be your wife and tak her at her will
   Doon by the burnie on the Braes o Bonald.

3. But noo ma freens, I'm sorry for tae say,
   Ma steps are growin shorter and ma hair is turnin grey.
   But if you'll come alang wi me, we'll hae anither gill
   And we'll drink the toast o Scotland on the Braes o Bonald.

* CHORUS repeats complete melody

40. Marnan Fair

sung by Jimmy MacGregor, Perth

Ma freens that's gai - thered here this nicht, jist
lis - ten for a wee, An I'll tell ye o a
lass I like an I'm sure that lass likes me. Ye could
search the toon an ne - ver fin a bon - ni - er lass I'm
shair, An I met her owre at Fog - gie - loan the

CHORUS

nicht o Mar - nan Fair. Then hur - rah ma boys, hur -
- rah! I've the life o a mair - ried man, An
I've been as hap - py as a king could be since I
mair - ried Ma - ry Ann. She's a pair o een as
ne'er were seen, an ring - lets o gol - den hair, An I
met her owre at Fog - gie - loan, the nicht o Mar - nan Fair.

2. We wandered owre the heather by the thistles and the sloe,
   Then in the evening, boys, I took her to a show.
   I bocht her candy in great lumps an she swore that it was rare,
   An I kissed the candy aff her lips on the nicht o Marnan Fair.

3. The first nicht I gaed hame wi her, the bottle was gey fu.
   The nicht that I gaed thon lang road, I'm sure I'll never rue.
   Her parents they gave me consent, and we hired a coach an pair,
   Gaed aff an we got mairrit on the nicht o Marnan Fair.

4. Twelve months noo are passed an gone and to crown oor earthly joys,
   I'll tell ye on the quiet we've been blessed wi a pair o boys.
   They're the very image o their Dad, so the neebours declare,
   An we're gaun tae open a baby show the nicht o Marnan Fair.

41. The Pear Tree

sung by Dave Marshall, Glencarse

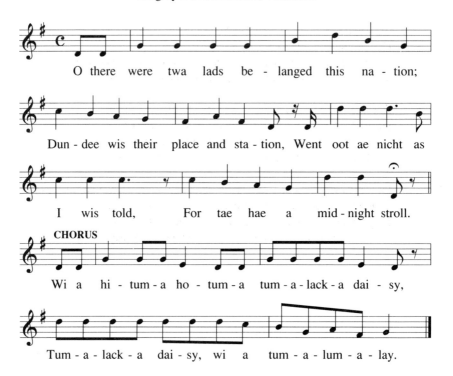

O there were twa lads be - langed this na - tion;
Dun - dee wis their place and sta - tion, Went oot ae nicht as
I wis told, For tae hae a mid - night stroll.

CHORUS

Wi a hi - tum - a ho - tum - a tum - a - lack - a dai - sy,
Tum - a - lack - a dai - sy, wi a tum - a - lum - a - lay.

2. For noo on the road they spied a pear tree,
   There grew pears as many as could be.
   So for a pear they were inclined
   And up the pear tree they did climb.

3. So far up the pear tree we were landed,
   Far up the pear tree we were stranded.
   It wisna the pears that taen my ee,
   But a lad an a lass in alow the tree.

4. So this young man began tae unlace her,
   This young man began tae embrace her.
   He's taen aff his coat tae save her goon
   When aa the pears come a-rummlin doon.

5. So this young man he looked up in wonder,
   As we battered doon the pears like thunder.
   So up he got and awa did flee,
   Leavin his coat lyin in alow the tree.

6. For the owner of the coat we did enquire,
   The owner of the coat wis our desire.
   The owner of the coat we never found out,
   So we had a damned guid coat for nowt.

7. So noo aa ye lads, whaur e'er ye may be,
   Dinna gang coortin in alow a pear tree,
   For if ye do ye'll spoil the fun
   When aa the pears come a-rummlin doon.

42. The Beefcan Close

sung by Annie Watkins, Dundee

As I went up the O - ver - gate, I met Je - mi - ma Ross. O she winked at me wi the tail o her ee, In the mid - dle o the Beef - can Close.

CHORUS

Ric - ky doo dum day, doo dum day, Ric - ky dic - ky doo dum day.

2. I asked her who she stayed with
   And she said it was Mistress Bruce,
   An after that I got
   An invitation till her hoose.

3. When I went up the close that nicht,
   The stairs wis awfy dark,
   So I took my money fae my inside pooch
   An tied it tae the tail o ma sark.

4. When I went in the hoose that nicht,
   I owre tae the chair, sat doon,
   But she winked at me wi the tail o her ee,
   An said, "Come ben the room."

5. Now aa the nicht I dreamt I wis
   In the airms o Jemima Ross,
   But when I woke up I wis on ma back
   In the middle o the Beefcan Close.

6. Now aa ye lads and lasses here
   When ye gang oot for a lark,
   Jist be like me when ye're on a spree,
   Tie the money tae the tail o your sark.

7. And now my song is ended here,
   I hope you enjoyed it well,
   An when ye go up the Overgate,
   See and enjoy yersel.

43. The Tradesman's Plooin Match

sung by Jock Duncan, Pitlochry

I've been tae ploo-in match-es roon aa the coun-try-side, I've
seen them by the Dee, the Don an bon-ny Dev-eron side. But the
ane that will be heard a-boot for many a year an day, Is the
trades-man's ploo-in match at Hog-man-ay.

CHORUS

Whist! Hi, haud back Jean! haud up, whoa, stand! Haud
up your heid ma bon-ny loon, man Jock you're dae-in grand!

[SHOUT]

"Haud her up a-hint Tam!" ye'll hear the bil-lies say, At the
trades-man's ploo-in match at Hog-man-ay.

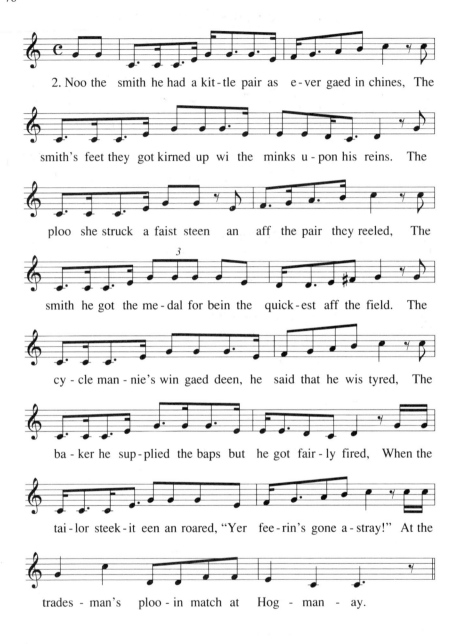

2. Noo the smith he had a kit-tle pair as e-ver gaed in chines, The

smith's feet they got kirned up wi the minks u-pon his reins. The

ploo she struck a faist steen an aff the pair they reeled, The

smith he got the me-dal for bein the quick-est aff the field. The

cy-cle man-nie's win gaed deen, he said that he wis tyred, The

ba-ker he sup-plied the baps but he got fair-ly fired, When the

tai-lor steek-it een an roared, "Yer fee-rin's gone a-stray!" At the

trades-man's ploo-in match at Hog-man-ay.

3. Noo the plumber he did lead the wye, aa efterneen he gassed,
   The souter he wis fairly soled, his name wis read oot last.
   The publican wis awfy tyawved his lan beast wis a balker,
   So he lowsed an bona-fied himsel wi a pint o Johnnie Walker.
   The postie had a chatterie rig, he trampit an he stampit,
   The slater he had tae retire fan baith his hands they crampit,
   The banker lost his interest when the bar closed for the day
   At the tradesman's plooin match at Hogmanay.

4. The fishman didna get a plaice, waur work I never saw, man.
   The gamie never turned a hare, his furs they lookit braw, man.
   The ice-cream mannie's cuttin ploo raised furs like hoky-poky,
   But the poultry merchant got the cup as wisna he gey cocky!
   For the best lookin plooman, the gairdner dressed sae braw,
   Got the ticket, he deserved it, the flooer amang them aa.
   An the brewer he gets brisk an stout and Younger every day
   At the tradesman's plooin match at Hogmanay.

5. The prizes read, the plooin match like aa thing else ye ken
   Wi speeches and gweedwillie chaff, it noo cam tae an en.
   The whisky on the barn fleer, it like cauld water ran,
   'Twis ladled into bowlies fae auld Hullie's berry pan.
   Wi bothy ballad, song an jest, the fun grew fast an furious;
   If ye've never been at a plooman's rant, an feel a bittie curious,
   Jist mind the date an dinna be late, be sure an wend your way
   Tae the tradesman's plooin match at Hogmanay.

44. The Dying Ploughboy

sung by Joe Aitken, Kirriemuir

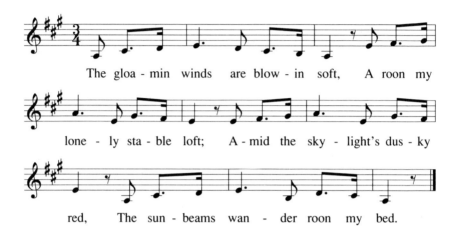

The gloa - min winds are blow - in soft, A roon my
lone - ly sta - ble loft; A - mid the sky - light's dus - ky
red, The sun - beams wan - der roon my bed.

2. The doctor left me in good cheer,
   But I've a feeling death is near;
   My time on earth has nae been lang,
   My time has come and I must gang.

3. Ah me, tis but a week the morn
   When I was weel and hairstin corn,
   As full of life and strength and fun
   As any man among the throng.

4. But something in my breist gaed wrang,
   A vessel burst and bluid it sprang,
   And as the sun sets in the sky,
   They lay me doon, nae mair tae rise.

5. Fareweel my horse, my bonny pair,
   I'll yoke an lowse wi you nae mair.
   Fareweel my ploo, wi you this hand
   Will turn in o'er nae mair fresh land.

6. Fareweel my friends, my comrades dear,
   My voice ye shall nae langer hear.
   Fareweel tae yonder setting sun,
   My time has come an I must gang.

7. I served my master weel and true;
   My weel dune work he willna rue.
   And yet for God I might have striven
   Tae reach the pearly gates of Heaven.

8. Tis weel my Maker knows my name.
   Will He give me a welcome hame?
   As I shall well hae need o hope,
   Receive me in thy mercy, Lord.

45. The Rovin Ploughboy

sung by John MacDonald, Pitgaveny

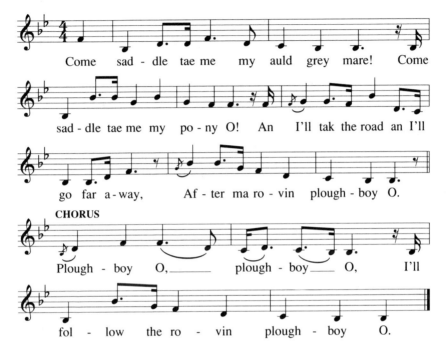

Come sad - dle tae me my auld grey mare! Come sad - dle tae me my po - ny O! An I'll tak the road an I'll go far a - way, Af - ter ma ro - vin plough - boy O.

CHORUS

Plough - boy O,____ plough - boy____ O, I'll fol - low the ro - vin plough - boy O.

2. Last night I lay in a fine feather bed,
   Sheet and blankets sae cosy O.
   Tonight I will lie in a cauld barn shed,
   Rowed in the airms o my ploughboy O.

3. A champion ploughboy, my Geordie lad,
   Cups and medals and prizes O.
   On bonny Deveronside there is nane tae compare
   Wi my jolly rovin ploughboy O.

4. What care I for the auld laird himsel,
   What care I for his siller O?
   Gae saddle tae me my auld grey mare,
   I'm awa wi the rovin ploughboy O.

5. So fare ye weel tae auld Huntly toon,
   Fare ye weel Drumdelgie O,
   For I'm on the road an I'm gaun far awa,
   Awa wi my rovin ploughboy O.

82

46. Grat for Gruel

sung by Jimmy MacBeath, Portknockie

There wis a wea-ver o the north, An o but he__ wis cru-el. The ve-ry first nicht__ that he got wad, He sat an grat for gruel.____ He wid-na wint his gruel, He wid-na wint his gruel o, The ve-ry first nicht__ that he got wad, He sat an grat for gruel.____

2. "There's nae a pot in aa the hoose,
   That I can mak yer gruel."
   "Oh the washin pot it'll dae wi me,
   For I maun hae ma gruel.
   For I maun hae ma gruel,
   I canna wint ma gruel,
   Oh the washin pot it'll dae wi me,
   For I maun hae ma gruel."

3. "There's nae a spune in aa the hoose
   That you can sup yer gruel."
   "Oh the garden spad it'll dae wi me
   For I maun hae ma gruel.
   For I maun hae ma gruel,
   I canna wint ma gruel,
   Oh the garden spad it'll dae wi me,
   For I maun hae ma gruel."

4. She gaed ben the hoose for cakes an wine,
   An brocht them on a tooel.
   "Oh gae wa, gae wa wi yer falderals,
   For I maun hae ma gruel.
   For I maun hae ma gruel,
   I canna wint ma gruel,
   Oh gae wa, gae wa wi yer falderals,
   For I maun hae ma gruel."

5. Come aa ye lassies tak my advice,
   An niver mairry a weaver.
   The very first nicht that he got wad,
   He sat an he grat for gruel.
   He widna wint his gruel,
   Oh he widna wint his gruel,
   The very first nicht that he got wad,
   He sat an he grat for gruel.

47. Bonny Ythanside

sung by Daisy Chapman, Aberdeen

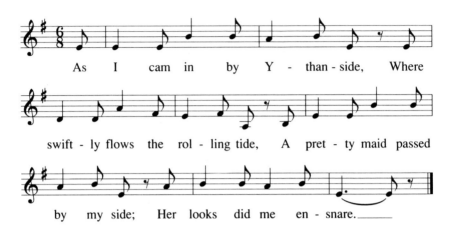

As I cam in by Y - than - side, Where
swift - ly flows the rol - ling tide, A pret - ty maid passed
by my side; Her looks did me en - snare._____

2. Sae I turned ma back on Fyvie's belles
   Tho ma poor heart gied mony a knell,
   An I speirt the road tae St. John's Wells
   Wi courage stoot and bold.

3. The maid turned roon wi'oot delay
   An this tae me began tae say,
   "I've scarcely been twa miles that way,
   Young man, I'll tell ye plain.

4. "But gin ye gang the gait ye came,
   I'll get a man tae show ye hame,
   Oot owre yon bonny flowery glen
   An doon by Ythanside."

5. Well, she took me tae her faither's hame,
   Sae bashfully as I gaed ben.
   Says he, "Young man, ye're far frae hame
   On bonny Ythanside."

6. Well, I sat doon her folk tae please,
   They treated me tae bread an cheese,
   The bairnies aa gaithered roon ma knees -
   It was a blythsome sight.

7. But the servant lads began tae spit
   An gaither aa up tae their fit.
   Thinks I, "Ma lads, ye're gaun tae flit
   An aa bound fur yer beds."

8. Sae up I got and straight ootricht
   And bid them aa a blythe guidnicht,
   And speirt the road tae Mains o Gicht
   Tae which the maid replied,

9. "Oh I'll show ye the barn door."
   Judge ye gin oor twa hearts were sore,
   Tae pairt that nicht tae meet nae more
   On bonny Ythanside.

10. But the lad came back soon in the Spring,
    Ay an on her finger placed a ring,
    An frae her hame he has her taen
    On bonny Ythanside.

11. This couple they've got mairrit noo,
    Ay an they hae bairnies yin or two,
    An as muckle land as keeps a coo
    On bonny Ythanside.

48. Bogie's Bonny Bell

sung by Tom Spiers, Aberdeen

Ae Whit-sun day in Hunt-ly toon, it's there I did a-gree, Wi Bo-gie-heid o Cair-nie a six month for tae___ fee; Tae drive his twa best hor-ses, like-wise his cairt an ploo An tae___ dee aa-thing a-boot fairm___work that___ richt weel I can do.

2. Noo, Bogie hid a dother whase name was Isabel,
   The flooer o her nation, there's nane her could excel;
   She hid rosy cheeks an ruby lips an hair o darkish hue,
   She wis neat, complete an handsome an comely for tae view.

3. One day she's wint oot walkin an chose me for her guide,
   Tae tak a pleasant walk wi her alang by Cairnieside.
   I've slipped ma airm aboot her waist an tae the grun did slide,
   An it's then I've haen ma first braw nicht wi the belle o Bogieside.

4. The blackbird sang sae sweetly an the mavis sang sae shrill,
   An aa the chorus o their sang was, "There lies Bogie's Bell."
   Amang the widds o Cairnie upon the grass sae green,
   Till she and I rose up again for fear we wid be seen.

5. Ere twinty weeks were past an gone, this lassie lost her bloom,
   Her rosy cheeks grew pale an wan an she began tae swoon.
   When forty weeks were past an gone, the lass brocht forth a son,
   An I wis quickly sent for tae see fit could be done.

6. Auld Bogie heard the story an cried, "I am undone!
   Since ye've beguiled ma dother, my sorrows are begun!"
   I said, "Auld man, ye're fairly richt," an I hung ma heid in shame,
   "I'll marry Bell the morn an I'll gie the bairn ma name."

7. Ah, but tho I said I'd wad the lass, "Na, na, that widna dee!
   Ye're nae a fittin match for Bell, nor she a match for ye."
   An he sent me packin doon the road wi nae penny o ma fee,
   Sae fareweel, ye lads o Huntly toon, a lang fareweel tae ye.

8. An noo she's mairried tae a tinkler chap wha's name is Soutar John,
   He hawks his pans an ladles aroon by Foggieloan.
   An maybe she's gotten a better match; auld Bogie canna tell,
   But 'twas me that taen the maidenheid o Bogie's bonny Bell.

49. Half Past Ten

sung by Robbie Shepherd, Dunecht

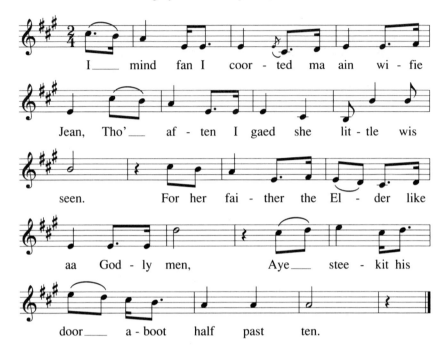

I___ mind fan I coor - ted ma ain wi - fie
Jean, Tho'___ af - ten I gaed she lit - tle wis
seen. For her fai - ther the El - der like
aa God - ly men, Aye___ stee - kit his
door___ a - boot half past ten.

2. The worthy man read, syne fervently prayed,
   An when he was dune he solemnly said,
   "It has aye been a rule - but 'tis likely ye ken
   That we steek aa oor doors aboot half past ten."

3. The hint wis eneuch for a blate lad like me
   But I catchit a bit blink o Jeanie's black ee,
   As much as tae say - "Come ye back tae the glen,
   An ye'll maybe stay langer than half past ten !"

4. Ae nicht twa-three lads an masel did agree
   Tae gang some place near jist tae hae a bit o a spree.
   Quo I, "What dae ye think o gaun doon tae the glen
   For we're sure tae be hame about half past ten."

5. We aa were receivit wi hearty guid will
   An the Elder no less broached a cask o his yill,
   Syne gae aff tae his bed an says, "Jean, ye'll atten'
   That the doors are aa lockit by half past ten."

6. "Oh aye," says Jean, but the best o the joke
   Was her steppin ben an stoppin the clock.
   I'm no gaun tae tell the hoo or the when,
   But the hauns werena pointin tae half past ten!

7. Aboot four in the mornin the auld man arose
   An lichtin a spunk, tae the clock straucht he goes.
   "Guid sauf us, guidwife, did ye hear me gae ben?
   Lod, the lads are awa afore half past ten!"

8. But the cat very soon wis let oot o the poke
   By the kecklin o hens an the craw o the cock,
   An openin the shutters he clearly saw then
   We wad aa hae oor breakfasts ere half past ten.

9. Ye ne'er heard sic lauchin aa the days o yer life
   An nane were sae hearty's the auld man an wife.
   Quo he, "What'll lassies no do for the men :
   Even cheat their ain faithers wi half past ten."

10. It wis settled then that Jean should be mine;
    The waddin sune followed an we've aye sin syne
    Lived happily thegither an hope tae the en
    We'll aye mind the nicht an its half past ten.

50. Drumdelgie

sung by Willie Clark, Ballindallach

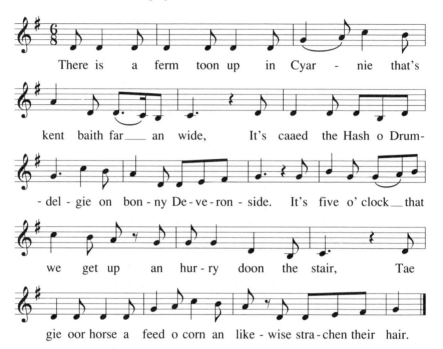

There is a ferm toon up in Cyar - nie that's kent baith far___ an wide, It's caaed the Hash o Drum- - del - gie on bon - ny De - ve - ron - side. It's five o' clock___ that we get up an hur - ry doon the stair, Tae gie oor horse a feed o corn an like - wise stra - chen their hair.

2. Half an oor in the stable, we each tae the kitchen go,
   Tae get some breakfast for oorsel which generally is brose.
   We've hardly time tae snap oor brose an gie wir p'ints a tie,
   When the gaffer lad says, "Hullo, ma lads, ye'll be nae langer nigh."

3. Wi sax o'clock the mill gaes on an hit gies aa stracht wark,
   For it's twal o hiz get wark at her till we could wring wir sark.
   An after mill is over, we aa rin up the stair
   Tae get the twa-three quarters throu the fan or daylicht does appear.

4. An when daylicht does appear, ma lad, an the sky begins tae clear,
   The grievie lad says, "Hullo, ma lads, ye'll stey nae langer here.
   For it's sax o you'll ging tae the ploo an sax tae caa the neeps,
   An the owsen will be efter ye wi nae strae up their queets."

5. Pitten on the harness an drawin it tae the yoke,
   The drift dung on sae very thick that we were like tae choke.
   An when the frost it did stick in an the ploo she widna go,
   We hid tae yoke the dung cairt amang the frost an snaa.

6. Drumdelgie teaches Sunday Skweel, an faith it is but richt,
   Tae preach untae the innocent the wey tae dae the richt.
   But we'll ging doon be Huntly toon an we'll get on the spree,
   An then the race it shall commence some quinies for tae see.

7. Fare ye weel Drumdelgie, I'll say goodbye tae you,
   Fare ye weel Drumdelgie, yer weet, weet weather an aa.
   Fare ye weel then Drumdelgie, I'll say goodbye tae you,
   An I'll leave ye as I got ye, a maist unceevil crew.

51. Granny Fraser's Flitting

sung by Ron Bisset, Fife

It was on a Mon - day mor - ning,___ and
weel I mind the scene, When my Gran - ny Fra - ser
flit - ted___ fae A - boyne tae Ai - ber -
- deen. The vil - lage folk they aa turned oot tae
see her on the road. The horse it could - nae
pu the cairt, ye should hae seen___ the load.

2. There wis airmchairs, bath chairs, rockin chairs as weel,
   Cradles an ladles, a pram withoot a wheel,
   Woollen shawls, moth balls, jeely pans an jars,
   An Grandpa near collapsed aneath Granny's chest o drawers.

3. There wis wee pots an stew pots an bonny wallie jugs,
   Flooer pots an stew pots an Granny's cheeny dugs,
   Wee pots an whatnots, ye'll ken the kind I mean,
   At Granny Fraser's flitting frae Aboyne tae Aiberdeen.

4. John McNab, the polisman, he called for volunteers;
   It wis the first time he had his jaiket aff for years.
   Tae get the donkey movin, every man did play his pairt,
   But halfway up the bloomin street the wheel fell aff the cairt.

5. There were face towels, enamel bowles litterin the street,
   Lace frocks, alarm clocks roon aboot their feet,
   There wis golf clubs an wash tubs litterin the lane
   An Grandpa's Ne'erday bottle nearly runnin doon the drain.

6. There were fur coats an porage oats mixed up in the glaur,
   Big spears an head gear o aa the Zulu wars,
   There wis antiques an tight breeks o 1817,
   At Granny Fraser's flitting frae Aboyne tae Aiberdeen.

7. Geordie Broon, the blacksmith, he weighed near twenty stane,
   He lifted up the cairt himsel, an put the wheel back on.
   We got the load securely tied amid the scoffs an jeers
   An when the lorry left the street, it got three rousin cheers.

8. There was auld spats an tile hats, sew a bag a day,
   Auld trays, auld claes she wouldna throw away,
   There wis floor mops and cough drops for Granny's wheezy chest
   An bottles o some nippy stuff ma Granny liked the best.

9. There wis lawn mowers an plus fours tied on wi a rope,
   An auld flag some lad tied ontae the top,
   On the tail board, encored, lookin like a queen
   Wis Granny Fraser sittin aa the road tae Aiberdeen.

52. I'm No Comin Oot the Noo

sung by Tommy Bonthrone, Auchenblae

A nice wee lass, a bon-ny wee lass is

bon-ny wee Jean-nie Mc-Kay.___ A ni-cer lass than

Jean-nie you would ne-ver ne-ver spy.___ I

said that I would take her to a mu-sic hall you see,___ So

dressed up nice and tric-ky___ she cam dan-cin roon for

me.___ But as she knocked u-pon the door I wis sor-ry I

CHORUS

had tae roar: "I'm no co-min oot the noo the noo, I'm

no co-min oot the noo.___ I'm aw-fy sor-ry Jean-nie___ for

dis-ap-poin-tin you.___ Ma mi-ther's taen ma

claes tae the pawn tae raise a bob or two, An I've on-ly a muff-ler

roon ma neck, so I'm no co-min oot the noo."___

© The Hardie Press 1995

2. I bought a nice new raincoat from a man called Mr Sleek.
   I said that I wad pey it at hauf a croon a week.
   I paid the first instalment, that is all he got you see,
   So next day he sent a lawyer's letter roon tae me.
   "Come roon an pey me for ma coat!"
   And in reply to him I wrote:

   CHORUS
   I'm no comin oot the noo, the noo, I'm no comin oot the noo,
   Tho you sent a lawyer's letter roon tae me it is true.
   I forged a cheque an I got the nick, so toora-loora-loo,
   In ten years time I may get oot, but I'm no comin oot the noo.

3. In a grand hotel where I reside the service is a treat,
   For every night the fleas come oot when I'm ablow the sheet.
   I couldnae get a wink o sleep, it really was a shame,
   So I bought some Keating's Powder just to spoil their little game.
   Last night when I got into bed,
   A million little voices said:

   CHORUS
   O we're no comin oot the noo, the noo, we're no comin oot the noo,
   You put some Keating's Powder on the bedclothes it is true.
   An if we came oot we'd aa be killt an that would never do,
   But we'll hae revenge some ither nicht, but we're no comin oot the noo.

53. The Auld Meal Mill

sung by Adam Young, Forfar

When the horse are in the sta - ble⸺ an the kye are in the byre,⸺ And the hard day's toil is o - ver⸺ and the auld folks round the fire.⸺ It is then I gang a trip - pin⸺ tae the fairm be - yond the hill,⸺ Jist tae meet ma win - some las - sie⸺ by the auld meal mill.

CHORUS

By the auld meal mill, by the auld meal mill, Jist tae meet ma win - some las - sie⸺ by the auld meal mill.

2. She's got een like bramble berries, she's got teeth like mountain snow,
   She has lips as red as roses, she's the sweetest flooer that grows,
   An I'm longing for the lowsin just tae quit the langsome drill
   An get aff tae see ma lassie, by the auld meal mill.
   By the auld meal mill, by the auld meal mill,
   An get aff tae see ma lassie by the auld meal mill.

3. Noo the auld folk aften wonder at whit keeps me oot sae late,
   For nane o them will gyang tae sleep till they hear me sneck the gate,
   But the auld lad he jalouses as I'm tripping owre the hill,
   That I'm aff tae meet ma lassie by the auld meal mill.
   By the auld meal mill, by the auld meal mill,
   That I'm aff tae meet ma lassie by the auld meal mill.

98

54. Princie and Jean

sung by Tam Reid, Echt

I'll sing ye a sang o a can - ty auld bo - die, A ken - speck - le fi - gure wis auld Wat - tie Broon. A trust - wor - thy hand at the Mains o Drum - clo - dy, Since the day he be - gan tae work there as a loon.

2. And syne there as bailie he proved himsel canny,
   His wark conscientious, particular and clean,
   Till ae day his maister said, "Wattie, ma mannie,
   Ye'll tak the third pair; they're caaed Princie and Jean."

3. And in bonny Scotland there wisnae a human
   Sae happy as Wattie wi his dandy pair,
   He seen held his ain wi the lave o the ploomen
   And oh, wis he prood o his geldin an mare!

4. A grand pair o blacks, nae their likes in a hunner,
   Wi coats o a rich glossy ebony sheen,
   And at plooin matches for years they were winners
   For groomin wis Wattie wi Princie and Jean.

5. So Wattie's aye bided content wi his duties,
   But life's fu o changes as aabody kens.
   Decrepit auld age claimed the pair o his beauties,
   An tractors begon tae be seen at the Mains.

6. Noo a steerin wheel Wattie jist widna be grippin;
   He wrocht on as orra-man, didnae compleen,
   But aabody noticed doonhill he wis slippin,
   Doonhill he wis pinin for Princie and Jean.

7. And noo he's awa, his trauchles are ended,
   A God-fearin bodie that aye did his best.
   His life wis a sermon - the mourners aa kent it
   On Tuesday last week when we laid him tae rest.

8. But we aa had a thocht, tho we didna divulge it,
   As wi hankies we dabbit the tears fae oor een:
   If He wha was born in a manger so wills it,
   They'll be waitin for Wattie - his Princie and Jean.

55. Cock-a-doodle-doo

sung by George McWilliam, Elgin

Ae Set-ter-day ef-ter-nune,_____ I gaed oot for a walk,_____ I walk'd right up the
(v.4)
O-ver-gate till I came u-pon a shop._____ The la-dy wis sel-lin birds,_____ she wis sel-lin her fi-nal stock,_____ I han-ded her a half a croon, she

CHORUS

han-ded me a Cock-a-doo-dle-doo,_____ it's no-thin to do wi you, It's a jol-ly fine bird an it's all I've got, It's ma cock-a-doo-dle-doo!

2. I thocht I wid tak it hame so I stuffed it in ma coat.
   I hadnae gone sae very faur when the cock began tae craw.
   A wifie wis passin by, she got such an awfy shock;
   Says she, "Hcy Jock, ma lad, ye're gaun tae lose yer ..."

3. Tae get ma rooster hame I got ontae a bus.
   I sat doon in a corner seat awa fae aa the fuss.
   The folk cam crowdin on, I squeezed up tae the top,
   "Excuse me, madam," I shouted, "ye've sat doon on ma ..."

*4. I went oot in a boat, the boat began tae rock,
   I fell intae the water an a fish got haud o ma ...

5. But at last I got it hame, I stuck it in a cage
   Beside an auld grey feathered hen - they baith flew in a rage.
   The wifie next door cam in, says she, "What's the maitter, Jock?"
   Says I, "That auld grey feathered hen is scratching aa ma ..."

   * Singer only sang 2 lines for this verse. The melody begins on
   the final note of line 3.

56. The Laird o Tomintoul

sung by Willie MacKenzie, Elgin

Noo I am a swell as ye can tell, a swell o so - ci - e - ty. Aye, ev - e - ry bo - dy is ef - ter me, I'm one o the a - ri - sto - co - ra - cy. When I ap - pear the peo - ple they cheer, an they raise their hats tae me._____ U - pon the street, I'm hard tae beat, for po - pu - la - ri - ty.__

CHORUS

Wi_____ ma stick in ma han noo I walk a - long wi an in - de - pen - dent air, The peo - ple I meet u - pon the street at me be - gin tae stare. Far - e - ver I go, they shout "Hul - lo!" an then be - gin tae howl: "There's Dou - gal Mc - Har - dy Mac - In - tyre, the Laird o Tom - in - toul!"_____

2. Noo the cannibal king wi his nose in a ring he held a grand review.
   Noo I wis there as large as life; aye, me an masel an the bobby's wife.
   The king he cried when me he spied,"My word, upon my soul,
   Why there gaes ma auld freen Macintyre, the Laird o Tomintoul!"

3. Noo the toffs frae the Sooth they come up tae shoot grouse
      an they pay a visit tae me.
   They pose wi me for ma photygraph an they pays me a pound
      for an autygraph.
   When it's time tae gae hame it's an awfy shame for the weemin
      they scream an they howl,
   But I waves them ta-ta as they drags them awa frae the
      Laird o Tomintoul.

57. It's Aa Wan Tae Me

sung by Sandy Watt, Glenfarg

O ma fai-ther bocht a horse, ma mi-ther a coo, Ma
bri-ther a boar an ma sis-ter a soo.

CHORUS

An it's aa wan tae me whe-ther I mair-ry noo or
no. Mair-ry or tair-ry, bide as I be. It's
aa wan tae me whe-ther I mair-ry noo or no.

2. My faither bocht a cock, ma mither a hen,
   My brither a robin an ma sister a wren.

3. My faither bocht a rat, ma mither a moose,
   My brither a bug an ma sister a louss.

4. We get work fae the horse, milk fae the coo,
   Gruntin fae the boar an piglets fae the soo.

5. We get crawin fae the cock, eggs fae the hen,
   Chirpin fae the robin an whistlin fae the wren.

6. We get gnawin fae the rat, nibblin fae the moose,
   Luikin for the bug an searchin for the louss.

58. The Irish Boy

sung by Phyllis Martin, Dumfries

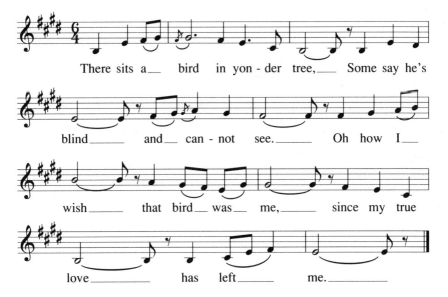

There sits a— bird in yon - der tree,— Some say he's
blind—— and— can - not see.—— Oh how I—
wish—— that bird— was— me,—— since my true
love———— has left—— me.————

CHORUS*
And it's oh! what a foolish young girl was I
To fall in love with an Irish boy.
An Irish boy he may well be,
But he spoke braid Scots when he coorted me.

2. I wish, I wish, but I wish in vain,
   I wish I were a maid again.
   But a maid again I'll never be
   Till apples growe on an orange tree.

3. I wish, I wish my babe was born
   And sittin on my mither's knee,
   And I, poor girl, was dead and gone
   Wi the long green grass growin owre me.

4. I leaned my back against an aik
   Thinkin it was a trusty tree,
   But first it bent and then it broke
   Just as my true love did unto me.

*CHORUS repeats complete melody

59. Wha'll Mowe Me Noo?

sung by Gordeanna McCulloch, Glasgow

2. Oor dame can lay her ain guidman,
   And mowe for glutton greed,
   And yet miscaws a young thing
   That's mowin for its breid.

3. Oor dame hauds up her ain guid tail
   As due as she gaes lie,
   And yet miscaws a young thing
   The trade if she but try.

4. Alack, sae sweet a tree as love
   Sic bitter fruit should bear.
   Alack, that sic a merry airse
   Should draw a sautie tear.

5. But deevil damn the lousy loon
   Denies the bairn he got,
   And leas the merry airse he loed
   Tae wear a raggit coat.

60. The Echo Mocks the Corncrake

sung by Sheila Douglas, Scone

O the lass that I loed best of aw was
hand-some young and fair. Wi her I spent some
mer-ry nichts u-pon the banks o Ayr; Wi
her I spent some mer-ry nichts whaur
yon wee bur-nie rows, And the e-cho mocks the
corn-crake a-mang the whin-ny____ knowes.____

2. We loved each other dearly an disputes we seldom had;
As constant as the pendulum oor hairt beats always gaed.
We socht for joy an found it whaur the scented clover growes,
An the echo mocks the corncrake amang the whinny knowes.

3. Ye ladies aw an pleasure dames, drive tae the banks o Doon,
Ye'll dearly pey for every scent tae the barber for perfume,
But rural joy is free tae aw whaur the scented clover growes,
An the echo mocks the corncrake amang the whinny knowes.

4. The corncrake is noo awa, the burn is tae the brim,
The whinny knowes are clad wi snaw that taps the highest whin,
But when cauld winter is awa an simmer clears the sky,
We'll welcome back the corncrake, the bird of rural joy.

61. The Belt Wi Colours Three

sung by Alison McMorland, Girvan

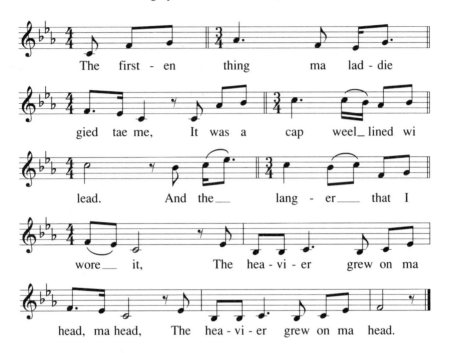

The first - en thing ma lad - die gied tae me, It was a cap weel‿ lined wi lead. And the‿ lang - er‿ that I wore‿ it, The hea - vi - er grew on ma head, ma head, The hea - vi - er grew on ma head.

2. The neisten thing oh ma laddie gied tae me,
   It was a mantle wi sorrow lined.
   I will wear that black mantle
   Till one to borrow I find, I find,
   Till one to borrow I find.

3. The thirden thing oh ma laddie gied tae me,
   It was a belt wi colours three.
   The first shame, the next sorrow
   And last of all sad misery,
   And last of all sad misery.

4. Now I maun climb as high a tree yet,
   And herry a far far richer nest
   And come down without falling.
   And mairry the lad that I loe best,
   And mairry the lad that I loe best.

5. But why should ye now climb a tree, may?
   Or pu the cherries ere they be ripe?
   For if the gairdner yince does see you,
   He'll throw you owre yon garden dyke,
   He'll throw you owre yon garden dyke.

6. Then up she rose and gaed on slowly,
   And stately stepped owre yon lea;
   And by the samen, it is weel kennin,
   That mourners crave nae company,
   That mourners crave nae company.

62. Tail Toddle

sung by Hamish Henderson, Edinburgh

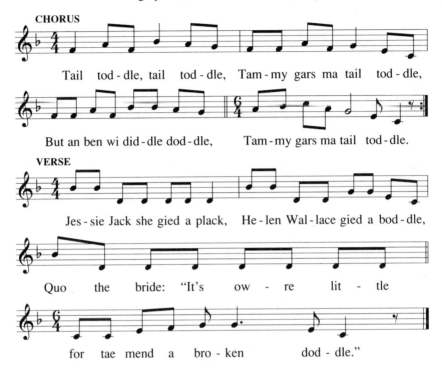

CHORUS

Tail tod - dle, tail tod - dle, Tam - my gars ma tail tod - dle,

But an ben wi did - dle dod - dle, Tam - my gars ma tail tod - dle.

VERSE

Jes - sie Jack she gied a plack, He - len Wal - lace gied a bod - dle,

Quo the bride: "It's ow - re lit - tle

for tae mend a bro - ken dod - dle."

2. Oor guidwife gaed owre tae Fife for tae buy a coal riddle,
   Lang or she cam back again, Tammy gart ma tail toddle.

3. Twa an twa made the bed, twa an twa lay doon thegither,
   When the bed began tae heat, the teen lay oot abeen the tither.

4. Fan I'm deid I'm oot o date, fan I'm seik I'm fu o trouble,
   Fan I'm weel I stap aboot an Tammy gars ma tail toddle.

110

63. Dae Ye Mind Lang Lang Syne?

sung by Janet Weatherston, Edinburgh

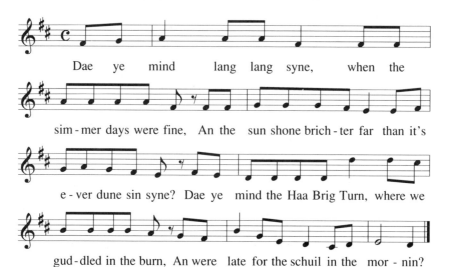

Dae ye mind lang lang syne, when the
sim - mer days were fine, An the sun shone brich - ter far than it's
e - ver dune sin syne? Dae ye mind the Haa Brig Turn, where we
gud - dled in the burn, An were late for the schuil in the mor - nin?

2. Dae ye mind the sunny braes where we gaithered hips an slaes
   An fell amongst the bramble bushes tearin aw oor claes,
   An for fear we wid be seen, we gaed slippin hame at een
   But were lickit for oor pains in the mornin?

3. Dae ye mind the miller's dam when the frosty winter cam
   An we slid across the curlers' rink an made their game a sham?
   When they chased us throu the snaw, we gied them leg bail, yin and aw,
   But we did it owre again in the mornin.

4. Oh what famous fun was there wi oor games o hoond an hare,
   When we played truant fae the schuil because it wis the Fair.
   When we ran fae Patie's Mill, throu the wuds tae Winning Hill,
   An were feart for the tawse in the mornin.

5. Oh where are these bricht herts noo that were aye sae leal an true?
   Some hae left life's troubled scene, some still are strugglin throu,
   An some hae risen high in life's changeful destiny -
   For they rose wi the lark in the mornin.

6. Oh oor sweet spring is past, and oor autumn's come at last,
   Oor simmer day has passed away, life's winter's comin fast;
   An tho lang the nicht may seem, we will sleep withoot a dream
   An we'll wake on yon bricht Sabbath mornin.

64. 'Twas Up Yon Dark and Stormy Glen

sung by George Gall, Auchtermuchty

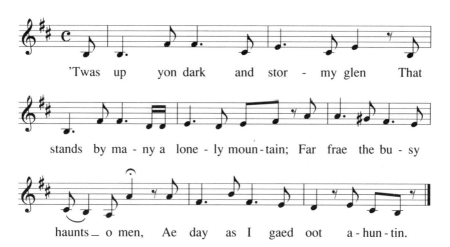

'Twas up yon dark and stor - my glen That
stands by ma - ny a lone - ly moun - tain; Far frae the bu - sy
haunts _ o men, Ae day as I gaed oot a - hun - tin.

2. A happy day it was tae be
   That day she stole my rovin fancy;
   She was herdin sheep on yonder hill,
   It was there I spied my lovely Nancy.

3. Her coat was white, her goon was green,
   Her waist it was so tall and slender.
   Wi her rosy cheeks an her downcast eyes,
   She made my hert nae mair tae wander.

4. Says I, "My lassie will ye gang,
   An sleep upon my bed o feathers?
   For it's silks an satins ye'll gang in
   If ye leave yer sheep amang the heather."

5. "Oh I thank you, sir, yer offer's fair,
   But I'm afraid it's meant in laughter;
   For you must be some rich squire's son,
   An I'm only a puir shepherd's dochter."

6. I hae been tae balls and masquerades,
   I hae been tae London and Balquhidder.
   But the bonniest lass that e'er I saw,
   It was her I met amongst the heather.

7. Oh it's her I sought and her I got,
   An wi her I mean tae live contentit.
   It's her I got and it's her I sought,
   So fareweel, fareweel, my story is ended.

65. The Band o Shearers

sung by Jack Beck, Dunfermline

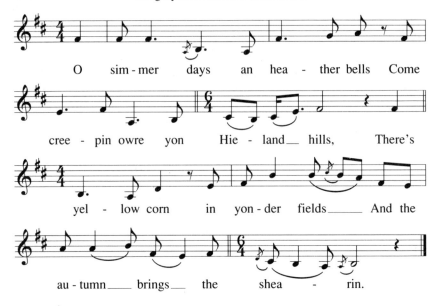

O sim-mer days an hea-ther bells Come cree-pin owre yon Hie-land— hills, There's yel-low corn in yon-der fields____ And the au-tumn____ brings____ the shea - rin.

CHORUS*
Bonny lassie, will ye gang
An shear wi me the haill day lang?
An love will cheer us as we gang
Tae jine yon band o shearers.

2. An if the thistle it be strang,
   An if it jag your milk-white hand,
   It's wi ma heuk I'll cut it doon
   When we jine yon band o shearers.

3. An if the weather it be hot,
   I'll cast ma gravat and ma coat,
   An shear wi you amang the lot
   When we jine yon band o shearers.

4. An if the weather it be dry,
   They'll say there's love twixt you and I,
   But we'll slyly pass each ither by
   When we jine yon band o shearers.

5. An when the shearin it's aa dune,
   We'll hae some rantin rovin fun;
   We'll hae some rantin rovin fun
   An forget the toils o the shearin.

6. Bonny lassie, fresh an fair,
   Will you be mine forever mair?
   If you'll be mine, then I'll be thine
   An we'll gang nae mair tae the shearin.

*CHORUS repeats complete melody

66. False, False Hae Ye Been

sung by Sheila Stewart, Blairgowrie

False___ false hae___ you been tae me___
___ my___ love, How of - ten ye've
chan - ged yer mind._____ But since
you've laid your love___ on a - noth-er fair___
maid,_____ I'm a - fraid you're
no___ more___ mine._____

2. I will climb into a tree that is too high for me,
   Seeking fruit where there weren't any growin.
   I was liftin warm water oot aneth cauld clay
   And against the stream I was rowin.

3. O but I mean tae climb up a far higher tree,
   Tae herry a white snowflake's nest.
   O an doon shall I fall, withoot any fear,
   Tae the arms that love me the best.

67. Love and Freedom

sung by Mary Brooksbank, Dundee

As I cam owre Strath - mar - tine Mains,

wha dae ye think I seen? A__ braw young pi - per

CHORUS

lad - die cam a lin - kin owre the green. Sing - in

hey Do - nald, ho Do - nald, di - rum a doo a day.

2. He played a reel and he played a jig and he played a sweet strathspey;
   He roosed ma hert till its beat skipped time tae the tappin o ma tae.

3. "Well I've nae gowd tae offer ye; I hae but little gear.
   But we'll hae love and freedom if ye follow me, my dear."

4. "There's gowd in the broom o the Sidlaw Hills, honey in the heather sweet.
   There's a speckled trout in the Henlinn Tarn, a velvet cairpet neath oor feet."

5. Syne he blew up his chanter an sic a spring he plays,
   So I chose love and freedom; I'll wander aa ma days.

68. The Tamosher

sung by Betsy Whyte, Montrose

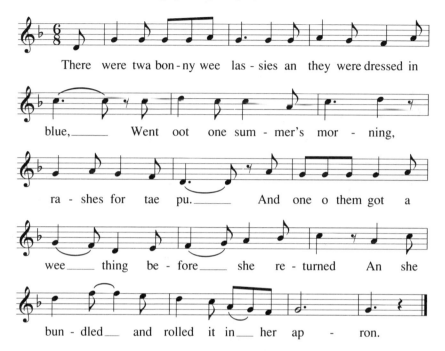

There were twa bon-ny wee las-sies an they were dressed in blue,_____ Went oot one sum-mer's mor - ning, ra - shes for tae pu._____ And one o them got a wee_____ thing be - fore_____ she re - turned An she bun - dled_____ and rolled it in_____ her ap - ron.

2. Noo the very first man she met wis her faither on the stair,
   "Oh dochter, oh dochter, whit hae you got there?
   Wha gae tae you the tamosher tae wear a starched gown,
   An you bundled it an rolled it in your apron?

3. "Oh wis it tae the baker or wis it tae the clown,
   Or wis it tae the bonny boy that sails the world around,
   That gave tae you the tamosher tae wear the starched gown,
   An you bundled it an rolled it in your apron?"

4. "Oh it wisnae tae the baker, nor wis it tae the clown,
   But it wis tae the bonny boy wha sails the world around,
   Wha gae tae me the tamosher tae wear the starched gown
   An I bundled it an rolled it in ma apron."

5. Noo there goes little Molly when she is in the town,
   Wi her riggy rocky slippers and the newly starched gown,
   Wi her riggy rocky slippers and the newly starched gown
   An she bundled it an rolled it in her apron.

69. The Rigs o Rye

sung by Dennis Findlay, Glasgow

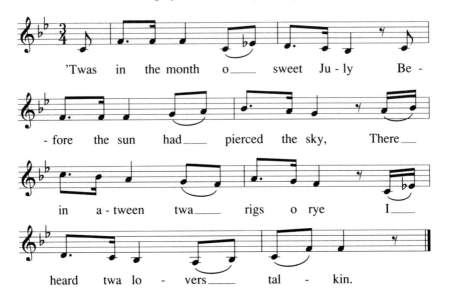

'Twas in the month o___ sweet Ju-ly Be-
- fore the sun had___ pierced the sky, There___
in a-tween twa___ rigs o rye I___
heard twa lo - vers___ tal - kin.

2. He said, "My dear, I must away,
   I have nae longer time to stay,
   But I've a word or two to say
   Gin ye hae the time tae tarry.

3. "Your faither o ye he taks great care,
   Your mither kaims doon your yellow hair,
   But your sisters say that ye'll get nae share
   Gin ye gang wi me, a stranger."

4. "Let my mither fret an my faither froon,
   My sisters twa I do disown.
   If they were deid and alow the grun,
   I wad gang wi you, a stranger."

5. "Oh lassie, lassie, your fortune's smaa
   An maybe it may be nane at aa.
   Ye're no a match for me ava,
   Lay your love, lass, on some ither."

6. The lassie's courage began to fail,
   Her rosy cheeks they grew wan an pale,
   An her tears cam trinklin doon like hail
   Or a heavy shower in the simmer.

7. He's tane his kerchie o linen fine,
   He's dried her tears, an he's kissed her syne.
   Sayin, "Lassie, lassie, ye shall be mine,
   I said it aa but tae try ye!"

8. This laddie bein o a courage bold,
   A gallus chiel just nineteen years old,
   He's gane the hills an the valleys o'er
   An the bonny lassie's gane wi him.

9. This couple they are mairrit noo,
   An they hae bairnies yin or two.
   They bide in Brechin the winter throu,
   Aye, and in Montrose in the simmer.

70. My Last Farewell to Stirling

sung by Charlie Murray, Forfar

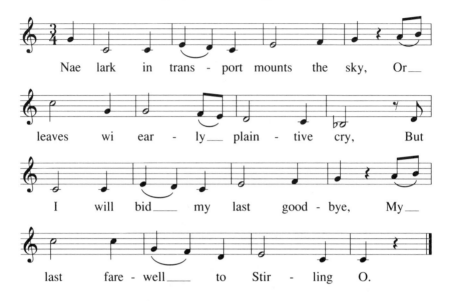

Nae lark in trans - port mounts the sky, Or__
leaves wi ear - ly__ plain - tive cry, But
I will bid__ my last good - bye, My__
last fare - well__ to Stir - ling O.

CHORUS*
Tho far awa my hert's wi you;
Our youthful oors upon wings they flew,
But I will bid a last adieu,
A last farewell to Stirling O.

2. Nae mair I'll meet ye in the dark,
   Or gang wi you to the King's Park,
   Or raise the hare from oot their flap
   When I gae far frae Stirling O.

3. Nae mair I'll wander throu the glen,
   Disturb the roost o the pheasant hen,
   Or chase the rabbits tae their den
   When I gae far frae Stirling O.

4. There's one request before I go,
   An this is to my comrades all:
   My dog an gun I'll leave tae you
   When I go far frae Stirling O.

5. So fare ye well, my Jeannie dear;
   For you I'll shed a bitter tear.
   I hope you'll find another dear
   When I go far frae Stirling O.

6. So fare ye well, for I am bound
   For twenty years to Van Diemen's Land,
   But think of me an what I've done
   When I gae far frae Stirling O.

*CHORUS repeats complete melody

71. The Boys o Callieburn

sung by Willie Scott, Hawick

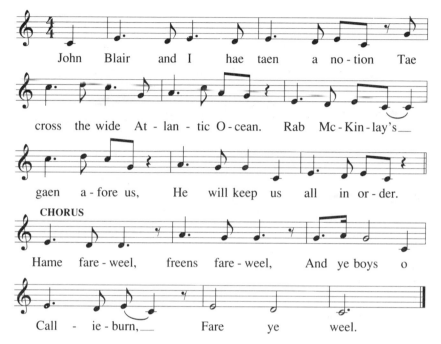

John Blair and I hae taen a no-tion Tae
cross the wide At-lan-tic O-cean. Rab Mc-Kin-lay's
gaen a-fore us, He will keep us all in or-der.

CHORUS

Hame fare-weel, freens fare-weel, And ye boys o
Call-ie-burn,__ Fare ye weel.

2. We leave the land of our forefathers,
   Knowing not what may befall us.
   America, 'twas thee that wiled us,
   For to leave our aged parents.

3. Machrihanish, bright and bonny,
   And on thy beach the waves are rolling.
   Machrihanish, I adore thee,
   Never more shall I be o'er thee.

4. We leave the land where we were born,
   Our parents they will ne'er disown us.
   This is a song of our own composing;
   Comrades dear, come join the chorus.

5. Mother dear, I'm going to leave you,
   Well I know that sore it grieves you.
   But mother dear, you may believe me,
   Till the day I die, I'll ne'er deceive ye.

72. The John McLean March

sung by Arthur Johnstone, Glasgow

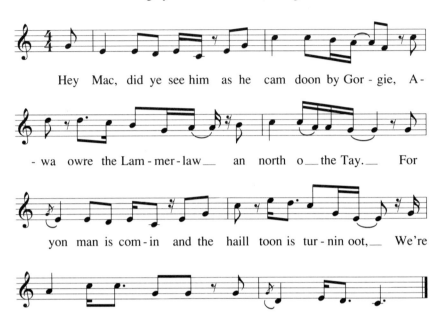

Hey Mac, did ye see him as he cam doon by Gor - gie, A-
- wa owre the Lam - mer - law __ an north o __ the Tay. __ For
yon man is com - in and the haill toon is tur - nin oot, __ We're
aw sure he'll win back tae Gles - ca the day.

2. The jiners and hauders-on they're mairchin fae Clydebank;
   Come on doon and see him - he'll be owre thrang tae bide.
   Come on, Jock and Jimmy, leave your crans and your muckle gantries,
   Great John McLean's comin hame tae the Clyde.

3. Argyle Street an London Road's the route that we're mairchin;
   The lads frae the Broomielaw are here tae a man.
   Hey Neil, whaur's your hadarums, ye big Hielan teuchter?
   Get your pipes, mate, and march at the heid o the clan.

4. Hallo, Pat Malony, we knew ye'd be here, son,
   The reid and the green, my lads, we'll wear side by side.
   The Gorbals is his the day and Glesca belangs tae him,
   Great John McLean's comin hame tae the Clyde.

5. Forward tae Glesca Green, we'll mairch in guid order,
   Will grips the banner weel, that boy isna blate.
   Look, man, that's Johnny noo, that's him, the bonny fechter,
   Lenin's his fere and Liebknecht's his mate.

6. Tak tent when he's speakin, for ye'll mind whit he said here,
   Tae Glesca, oor city, and the haill world beside.
   Look, man, the scarlet's bonny! Here's tae ye, Hielan Johnny!
   Great John McLean has come hame tae the Clyde.

7. Ah weel, when it's finished, I'll awa hame tae Springburn.
   Come hame tae your tea, John, we'll soon hae ye fed.
   It's hard work the speakin. I'm sure ye'll be tired the nicht;
   I'll sleep on the flair, Mac, and gie John the bed.

8. The haill city's quiet noo, it kens that he's restin,
   At hame wi his Glesca freens, their fame and their pride.
   The red will be worn again, and Scotland will rise again
   Noo great John McLean has come hame tae the Clyde.

Hamish Henderson

73. The Collier's Eight-Hour Day

sung by John Eaglesham, Glasgow

Now aw ye jol-ly col-li-er lads, come lis-ten un-tae me,_____ Ye know how we are sore op-pressed__ by mas-ter's ty-ran-ny. For th'im-prove-ment o wir mines nae__ lei-sure time is found, An our chil-dren are ne-glec-ted to be wor-kin un-der ground._____

CHORUS (to be sung after verses 2, 4, 6 and 7)

Mac-do-nald is the col-li-er's friend: by us, he true is found.____ He thinks eight hours is plen-ty for to work be-neath the ground._____

2. Oh! Masters are tyrannical, and that they must confess:
   They over-tax their workmen and do them sore oppress.
   Nae other occupation sae dangerous can be found;
   We cannot say our life's wir own while workin underground.

3. The sailor he does plough the main, and perils does go throu,
   But he sees the danger comin which a collier cannot do.
   Wi fallin roofs and fire damp, the records can be found
   How hundreds yearly lost their lives while workin underground.

4. Down in the bowels o the earth our livelihood we gain;
   Our wives and little families we toil for to maintain.
   Wi five shillins a day some people say we'll never lack a pound,
   But colliers cannot work full time, ye know, beneath the ground.

5. Now most o the trades and callins, wherever that we go,
   Have gained a short time movement, ye very well do know.
   And why should we poor colliers behind the rest be found?
   We think eight hours is quite enough to work beneath the ground.

6. Dalry, Kilbirnie, Johnstone, Kilmarnock and Ayr,
   Glasgow, Coatbridge, Airdrie and the whole of Lanarkshire,
   Falkirk, Fife and Gallowa and the Lothian men aw say
   That colliers should, like other men, but work eight hours a day.

7. Some useful books we will procure for to improve wir mind,
   Our health and recreation amang the fields we'll find.
   The leisure hours we have to spare will not be thrown away,
   And we'll pray for brave Macdonald that he's gained eight hours a day.

BACKGROUND NOTES TO SONGS

The references to CHILD and GD allude respectively to Francis James Child's *The English and Scottish Popular Ballads* and Gavin Greig and James B. Duncan's *Folk Song Collection* (Vols. 1–8).

1. **Johnnie Armstrang** (Child 169)

"The Armstrongs appear to have been in possession of a great part of Liddesdale and the Debateable Lands... At the head of a desperate band of freebooters, this Armstrong is said to have spread the terror of his name almost as far as Newcastle and to have levied Black Mail for many miles around. James V, about 1530, undertook an expedition through the Border counties to suppress the turbulent spirit of the Marchmen." (Sir Walter Scott, *The Minstrelsy of the Scottish Borders*). The ballad, which takes a more partisan view of the events, was learned by Willie Beattie from Dick Wilson of Newcastleton.

2. **Achanachie Gordon** (Child 239: 'Lord Saltoun and Auchanachie')

A North-East ballad learned by Joe Rae's grandfather from a comrade in the Gordon Highlanders during the Boer War. The name refers to an estate near Elgin held by the Gordon family. The situation in which a young heiress is forcibly married to a rich old suitor, although she may be in love with a younger and poorer man, reflects a society in which land and property were the most important considerations.

3. **The Baron o Brackley** (Child 203; GD Vol 2 No 234: 'The Baron o Braikley')

Reiving went on not only in the Borders between Scotland and England but in the border between Highland and Lowland. This is another ballad of the Gordon family. "Two historical incidents of 1592 and 1666 correspond in some respects to the narrative of the ballad." (GD vol.2 p.542). Ewan MacColl describes it as a rare piece commemorating an affray which took place on September 16th 1666, between John Gordon of Brackley, a petty baron of the family of Aboyne, and his neighbour Farquharson of Inverey, "a renowned freebooter in Deeside" as noted by Jamieson. Brackley is on Deeside near Ballater. The part played by the lady implies some treachery on her part.

4. **The Beggar Laddie** (Child 280; GD Vol 2 No 277: 'The Beggar's Dawtie')

This is one of several songs in which a nobleman or king disguises himself as a beggar. In the days when there were licensed beggars or gaberlunzies, anyone wishing to travel incognito might well put on such a guise. It could be interpreted in this case as an attempt to find a wife who would love him for himself and not his rank and riches. The tune is similar to the one used for the old song 'The Rigs o Rye', whose story resembles that of the ballad.

5. **Corachree** (GD Vol 7*)
    A North-East love ballad with local reference to Tarland and a down-to-earth story told with simplicity and freshness that avoids prurience. It has the same haunting quality as 'Bogie's Bonny Bell', whose tune, 'The Plains of Waterloo', it echoes and to whose time it seems to belong. Jimmy Hutchison learned it from Norman Kennedy. Ailie Munro says of the song, "Its origin has not been traced or any printed version found, but fear of the session clerk takes us back at least 160 years or so."

6. **The Bonny Hoose o Airlie** (Child 199; GD Vol 2 No 233)
    "Airlie Castle was destroyed in 1640 during Charles I's troubles with his subjects." (GD vol.2 p.264). The Earl of Argyle had been given "a commission of fire and sword" against Airlie, who was a royalist. The Charlie mentioned in the ballad has often been confused with Bonnie Prince Charlie a century later. Belle evidently takes it to be a Jacobite song as her version mentions Lochiel. The Stewarts of Blair have a connection with Airlie as old John Stewart, Belle's father-in-law, a notable piper, used to pipe and win medals at the Glenisla Games.

7. **Willie's Rare** (Child 215)
    Although Child combined this ballad with the one telling of 'Willie Drowned in Gamrie', Alexander Keith does not believe them to be the same ballad, even though they have verses in common, as the latter has more of a story than the former. The tune resembles that used for 'Barbara Allen'. This version has a literary flavour to it.

8. **Lord Randal** (Child 12; GD Vol 2 No 209)
    This ballad appeared in Scott's *The Minstrelsy of the Scottish Border* and there are English versions, as well as European ballads with a similar story everywhere from Scandinavia to Eastern Europe. Mabel Skelton herself believed it to have been written and sung by Henry VIII and while there is no evidence for this, although Greig recorded a version of it that referred to "King Henry my son...", it is clearly a ballad of some antiquity. The question and answer form is a very old ballad device and one that helps to build up dramatic effect.

* At the time of going to press this volume was still in preparation.

9.   **Andra Lammie** (Child 233; GD Vol 5 No 973)

Sometimes called 'Tifty's Annie' or 'The Trumpeter o Fyvie', this is one of the most popular ballads in the North-East and refers to actual events of 1673, when Agnes Smith was buried in Fyvie Kirkyard. The shortened version of the ballad sung nowadays misses out a good deal of the story, so it is worth looking it up in Child's collection, for it highlights many features of the social system of the time. Annie's father, noted for his cruel temper, had ambitions for his daughter to marry Lord Fyvie himself, not one of his servants. Lord Fyvie intercedes on Annie's behalf to persuade her father to let her marry his trumpeter, but to no avail. Jane Turriff's version has her dying of a broken heart, which is what is on her gravestone but other versions have her being beaten to death. Since the ballad came from local recollection of what happened, its different versions may reflect different opinions.The ruin of Mill of Tifty can still be seen and the stone figure of a trumpeter stands on the top of Fyvie Castle.

10.   **Hame Drunk Cam I** (Child 274; GD Vol 7)

The oldest version of this ballad is in Herd's collection of 1776 and his was the foundation of all subsequent printed versions. There is an English version called 'The Merry Cuckold and the Kind Wife'. There are also similar songs in many other languages and as recently as June 1993, I heard ten different examples sung by Judith Cohen of Toronto at the International Ballad Conference in Los Angeles. This is an example of a joke that is truly international. Cameron Turriff's version belongs unmistakably to the North-East and the late 19th century.

11.   **The Battle of Harlaw** (Child 163; GD Vol 1 No 112)

"The grim battle, fought in 1411, takes us back almost half a millenium to the time and occasion at once critical and inevitable when Lowlander and Highlander had to settle which of the two was to have political supremacy in Scotland." (GD vol.1 p.527). 'The Battle of the Hayrlau' is mentioned in *The Complaynt of Scotland* in 1549 and Ramsay included an old historical poem of the same title in *Evergreen*, but "All the time that editors in general were copying this pseudo-ballad into their collections, they might any day have heard in the North a genuine ballad on Harlaw sung to a genuine folk tune in the true traditional way." (GD vol.1 p.527). The tune appropriately is a pipe tune.

12.   **Alison Cross** (Child 35: 'Alison Gross')

This ballad of witchcraft obviously must date back very far in time, and is a version of the folktale 'Beauty and the Beast', which is found all over Europe. Many ancient beliefs feature in the story, such as the kiss of enchantment, which the hero refuses to receive, the use of wand and magic words and the delousing of his head by his sister as a token of affection. The blowing of the "grass-green horn" and the intervention of the Fairy Queen are unique to the Scots version of the ballad.

Lizzie's spine-tingling singing of it is unforgettable. She used the chorus only occasionally, not after every verse.

13. I Aince Hid a Lass

Also known as 'The Lost Bride'. There is a version of the song in Dean Christie entitled 'It hasna been my lot to get her', and in Ord's *Bothy Songs and Ballads* as 'It wasna my fortune to get her.' Elizabeth learned this ballad from her aunt, Lucy Stewart. This ballad was very popular in the Folksong Revival, a testament to the timelessness of its theme and human emotions. The pain of lost love is a universal sorrow.

14. Glenlogie (Child 238; GD Vol 5 No 1018)

Sometimes called 'Bonny Jeannie o Bethelnie'. The earliest extant version called 'Jean o Bethelnie', dated 1768, was sent to Thomas Percy, for his *Reliques of Ancient English Poetry*, but Child did not regard it as pure tradition, saying it "smacked of revision by chap-rhymsters." Yet other North-East versions are very similar. Some versions give her name as Jeannie Gordon (which it became in marriage, of course) but elsewhere she is called Meldrum or Melville. The occasion on which the story took place is reputedly when Mary Queen of Scots visited Banchory on one of her progresses through Scotland. In a time when daughters of the gentry rarely had a say in whom they would marry, Jeannie seems to have been an exception.

15. The Beggarman (Child 279: The Gaberlunzie Man; GD Vol 2 No 275)

This ballad first appeared in Ramsay's *Tea-table Miscellany* in 1724 and has been attributed to James V, who, as the 'Guidman o Ballengeich' was reputed to mingle with his subjects incognito. Beggars at one time were licensed to beg and gathered their alms in a satchel or gaberlunzie (the z represents the obsolete letter called yog, which was pronounced like the y in yes). This is related to 'The Beggar Laddie', as a story about a lady who falls in love with a beggar and finds he is a man of rank and wealth.

16. Dumfries Hiring Fair

This is a feeing market song from the South-West of Scotland of the type which concerns a bad place where the horses were poor, the food even worse and workers were treated badly. Its aim is satirical and it expresses the farmworkers' dissatisfaction in an age when there was no redress except to move on at term time. The Irish-sounding chorus, as well as the idiom of the invective, are typical of the area, showing it to be a local song, not one transplanted from elsewhere with the name of the fair changed.

17. The Diamond Jubilee

This seems to be a song for stage performance, a comic music hall song, probably one of many published as a songsheet to celebrate Queen Victoria's sixty glorious years. It shows the comic Scotsman was in vogue long before Sir Harry Lauder. It is noteworthy, however, that the song contains no reference to tartan, heather, haggis or whisky. Also, it does not sound as if it was written by a Scot, in spite of the reference to the Duke of Argyle.

18. The Packman (also called Wild Gallowa)

The song was published without a tune and the people of St John's Town of Dalry and Moniaive each have their own tune for it. Dave McFadzean prefers the former, that of 'Erin gu Brath'. It was printed by the Galloway poet Murray in his volume of verse, *Frae the Heather*, and was written by his son around the time of the Boer War. It tells a cautionary tale of a Galloway lad who thinks to better himself by going South and becoming a packman or door-to-door salesman, then discovers the drawbacks of the work and returns to his native hills, perhaps a common experience in the Industrial Revolution. Dave learned the song from Jo Miller and Dave Henderson.

19. I Must Away, Love

This is a night-visiting song that belongs to an age when houses were small and hours of work long, so that courtship had many problems. The custom of night-visiting differed from one part of the country to another, but basically it involved the man coming to his sweetheart's house at night, being discreetly admitted to spend the night with her (sometimes with a bolster between them) and departing before daybreak. There is no suggestion of seduction or rape in these songs : they are about clandestine meetings of true lovers. For another version, see No 27 'The Porter Laddie'.

20. Burke and Hare

This has all the marks of a broadside ballad from the time when William Burke and William Hare were tried in Edinburgh (1827-29) for the crime of murder to procure bodies for medical dissection in Dr. Knox's School of Anatomy at the University. There was no legal way at the time for anatomists to obtain subjects. Burke and Hare had progressed from selling already dead bodies to luring drifters into their High Street quarters and smothering them. There was a widespread fear of resurrectionists, as they were called, throughout Scotland, and gravewatchers' houses can still be seen in some old kirkyards.

21. Bonny Laddie, Ye Gang By Me

There is a song in Ord's *Bothy Songs and Ballads* called 'The days are awa that I hae seen' which bears resemblances to this one, and is thereby connected to the

'Lang a-growing' or 'The trees they do grow high' group of songs and also a song called 'My Laddie's Bedside' sung by Duncan Williamson on Scotsoun's *Folk Music Revival in Scotland* cassette that accompanies Ailie Munro's book of the same title. It is a song of lost or spurned love with all the hallmarks of a traditional song, such as its beginning, "It fell upon a day/In the merry month of May," to formulas like, "Ye micht hae coorted six/And ye micht hae coorted seiven/Ye micht hae coorted echt, nine, ten and eleiven." This version is more than a lament for lost love; it also retaliates against rejection, rather in the spirit of 'Mormond Braes'.

22.   The Weaver's Lamentation

This broadside ballad was first published around 1819, when the Glasgow authorities, nervous about all the popular assemblies, found work for the unemployed draining Glasgow Green as well as quarrying stone for the docks. The immediate source from which this was abbreviated was an Irish chapbook in the collection of Leslie Shepard. The decline of the handloom weaving industry in the early nineteenth century caused suffering and hardship to men whose skills were overtaken by machines. The deference shown to upper class people who thought they were helping skilled men to provide for their families by employing them to break stones - work traditionally associated with prisoners - shows the gulf that existed between the two social classes.The fact that some were from Ireland also illustrates what has been commonplace in West of Scotland society.

23.   Tattie Jock

A bothy ballad from the last century that is also a transportation ballad, from the days when people could be sent to Van Diemen's Land (Tasmania) for quite minor offences. It also highlights the poor working conditions of farm workers who were driven by hunger to steal from the farmer's tattie shed. It is worth noting that in other versions of this song the farmer regretted his anger in calling in the law when he realised that he had lost his entire workforce.The ballad is based on real events and real people and a farm that actually existed.

24.   The Collier Laddie

Ord quotes Burns as saying, "I do not know a blyther old song than this," which shows it to be of a good age. There is another song with a similar story called 'The Plooman Laddie', which may have preceded it. This must be one of the earliest songs to elevate the miner to the status of folk hero, along with the ploughman of rural life, and must also be one of our oldest industrial ballads. Irene Riggs comes from a mining family in Kirkcaldy and shows the strong attachment to such songs in the closeknit mining community.

25. Macpherson's Rant (GD Vol 3 No 697)

Davie Stewart's version of this favourite North-East song was "highly fluid and improvisatory" according to Hamish Henderson, who recorded him. While not typical of all singers of his generation, it is nevertheless reminiscent of the recreative techniques we know were widely used in the past. Jamie Macpherson was the son of a Highland laird and a travelling woman and is variously recorded as an incorrigible rogue and outlaw and as a kind of Robin Hood character, stealing from the rich to give to the poor. 'The Death of Singing Jamie' is a story in Katharine Briggs' *Folktales of the British Isles* and a very sympathetic account. He was famed as a musician, and when no-one offered to play his fiddle after he was gone, he broke it and threw it to the crowd around the gallows. He wrote a song in prison before he died, but this is not it. There have been many versions written and sung, including one by Burns to which this one seems fairly close. Davie had his own version of the chorus, usually rendered as :-

> Sae rantingly, sae wantonly, sae dauntingly gaed he,
> He played a tune and danced aroon alow the gallows tree.

26. The Donibristle Mossmorran Disaster

Donibristle Colliery was sited on the Moor of Mossmorran, south of Kinross and east of Dunfermline. The disaster took place on 26th August 1901. Engineers were drilling a ventilation shaft when a tremendous inrush of water shut off the workings. Although a party was lowered and was successful in rescuing several miners, it was then itself cut off. They tried to get through abandoned workings but were prevented by the stoppings put in to seal them off. The nine men gradually died for lack of oxygen. Messages to relatives, noted down by Thomas Rattray, the oversman, can still be seen in the Murison Burns collection in Dunfermline Public Library. The song was written by James R. Murray of Cowdenbeath. John Watt does not sing the song in the way he heard it, but alters the phrasing and tempo to point the words better.

27. The Porter Laddie

Another version of the night-visiting song (see No 19) and one learned by Jock Lundie in the bothy. The title might refer to the feeing market at Porter Fair at Turriff where the farm servants, such as the one featured in the song, might have been hired. As Jock was himself a ploughman and can still wink at the lasses at the age of 88, he can help us appreciate the ardour of the young man who could visit his sweetheart late at night and still be up for his work early in the morning.

28. Hatton Woods

This fresh, lyrical song seems to be a favourite with country singers in Perthshire, Angus and Aberdeenshire. The names Hatton and Caddam Woods occur in the area between Blairgowrie and Kirriemuir. The good-natured ploughman in the song, who certainly doesn't seem to have been well-treated by the girl he courted for "a twelvemonth and a day", shows a remarkable lack of bitterness towards her, blaming his own folly rather than her selfishness in rejecting him, because life in a cottar house does not appeal to her. It also sounds as if she has been gey lucky not to have ended up, as so many lasses in folk songs do, holding the baby. The tune is also well-loved and used for other songs.

29. Jamie Foyers (GD Vol 1 No 106)

This song, believed to have been composed by a John MacNeill, dates back to the Napoleonic Wars, in particular to the Peninsular Campaign in Spain in the early 1800s. A descendant of the Robert (thought to be, more correctly, David) Pirie mentioned in the song, discovered a copy of it among her grandfather's papers in the 1970s. It appeared in Robert Ford's *Vagabond Songs and Ballads of Scotland*, where it is recorded as a favourite song in the rural parts of Perthshire in the middle of the nineteenth century. Born at Campsie in Stirlingshire, James Foyers was a weaver before he enlisted as a volunteer from the Perthshire Militia to the 1st Battalion of the 42nd Regiment of Foot in June 1811 and was killed at the storming of Burgos Castle in September 1812. The tune Willie MacPhee sings is a variant of the first tune in the Greig-Duncan Collection (GD vol.1 no.106A).

30. The Magdalen Green

A Dundee song printed on a songsheet sold in the Poet's Box in the Overgate, this has been very popular in the Folk Revival. The Green itself is still to be seen, a pleasant grassy expanse near the riverside. Magdalen (pronounced locally "maidlin") survives from the name of a chapel dedicated to St. Mary Magdalen that used to stand in the vicinity and whose adjoining land became the Green. Dundee, which has a long history, became a very busy port for whaling ships, cargo boats bringing jute and fishing boats, and her Panmure Yard built Captain Scott's *Discovery*, which, along with the frigate *Unicorn*, is now one of the sights of the waterfront development. Sailors would be forever leaving and coming ashore and many of them must have walked with their lasses on the Green "on love and pleasure bent".This story however is quite unusual in that it is sung from the sailor's point of view. The happy ending is brought about in a magical way through a dream, and ends with the repentance of the young man for his treatment of the girl, that was "neither straight nor clean".

31. Jamie Raeburn

Greig noted this as "one of the most popular folksongs we have". Ford knew of it as "a popular song all over Scotland and readily sold in penny-sheet forms", about "a baker to trade who was sentenced to banishment for theft more than sixty years before". It had also appeared as a broadside under the title of 'The Hills of

Caledonia O'. This transportation ballad was still being sung when John Ord made his collection in 1925. It recalls the days when even minor offenders could be sent to penal colonies overseas, which meant parting from their families and loved ones. It is unlikely that many would return, for even if they survived the hardships and disease of places like Van Diemen's Land and Botany Bay, they would have to overcome the shame and stigma of being an ex-convict. Jamie Raeburn's farewell is so touching that it seems unlikely he was a hardened criminal. Like many who were transported, his "crimes" may have been the result of poverty and deprivation.

32.　The Banks o Inverurie

A broadside ballad found in Ord's collection and one of the large number of pastoral songs of courtship in which the young man has to overcome the girl's distrust. In this case, the rake's sudden reformation may leave lingering doubts in the mind of the listener, which could be increased with reference to Ord's version in which, as in some versions of 'The Jolly Beggarman':–

> He put a horn to his lips
> And he blew both loud and shrill,
> Till six and thirty armed men
> Came to their master's call.

Perhaps he was just showing her that he was a man of rank and substance, or providing a guard of honour for the wedding, but it would leave her little choice but to accept his proposal. At least he does seem to be sincere in his intent to marry her.

33.　Roy's Wife o Aldivalloch (GD Vol 4 No 748)

Gavin Greig notes that: "On 21st February 1727 John Roy, lawful son of Thomas Roy of Aldivalloch, was married to Isabella, daughter of Allister Stewart sometime resident in Cabrach". The original version of the song suggests "Roy's wife is scarce saxteen" and "Roy's thrice as auld," so no doubt she married him for his money, leaving her younger suitors to pine for her. The song is reputedly written by a Mrs Grant of Elchies, although one source says it was composed by a shoemaker. Robert Chambers in his book *Songs of Scotland Prior to Burns* reports that Peter Buchan preserves an old song with a verse :–

> Silly body Aldivalloch,
> Silly body Aldivalloch,
> He's fyled his hose and tint his sheen
> Comin o'er the Braes o Balloch.

Apparently, at one point Tibbie ran off with a younger man called David Gordon of Kirktown but was pursued and brought back by John Roy over the Braes of Balloch. It was on the basis of this that Mrs Grant produced her song which, according to Chambers, "purified an old vulgar song". Stanley learned this song from his aunt, the famous ballad singer, Jeannie Robertson, whose version is slightly altered from the one edited by Mrs Grant.

34. The P D Drifters

This homely song from the Peterhead fishing community expresses the joy of seeing the fishing fleet heading for home, with all the excitement of family reunions where presents were brought back for everyone. These were the happiest times for the fisherfolk, in contrast to the hard toil, separation, danger and heartbreak of the rest of their lives. The drift net fishermen were usually away for long periods and often the only news their families would have of them would be when a boat went down in a storm. Many wives and daughters worked in the gutting yards all down the east coast and in the Northern Isles, so they might be away too.

35. Brose Aa Day

Jock Weatherston learned this song from his grandmother, which suggests it dates back to well before the turn of the century. It satirises the monotony of the farm servants' diet which "generally was brose", a kind of porridge, with variations of oatmeal and kale, but never much else and certainly no meat. Eck Harley described brose as "Twa haunfuls o oatmeal and salt wi boiling water and milk", and confirms it is what the farm worker got for breakfast, dinner and tea. "There was a lot of work tae be done aff the brose". If a kitchie deem wanted to show favour to any of the bothy chiels she might, as in the much later song, 'Nicky Tams', "clart a muckle piece ... with different kinds of jams" – that would be a rare treat.

36. Eence Upon a Time

Ray Fisher learned this as a fragment from Jeannie Robertson, consisting of verses 1, 2 and 6 and added the other verses herself, which she felt were in keeping with the song. This demonstrates the creative approach that is required by traditional singing, in which text and tune are not sacrosanct; it also calls for a sympathetic understanding of the song, the situation and the feelings it deals with, such as Ray undoubtedly has. The girl's resolve to "find anither lad tae faither Johnnie's bairn" should not be seen as a sign of fickleness or loose morals but as practical concern for her child's welfare. This brings to mind the line from Violet Jacob's 'Up the Noran Water' set to music by Jim Reid, which says: "Up the Noran Water the country folk are kind/And wha the bairnie's faither is they dinna muckle mind."

37. New Ferm Toon

This song was written about Newton of Lathrisk Farm, near Falkland in Fife, about 1919 and was a typical song that was sung in the bothies. It pokes irreverent fun at all the servants on the farm without mincing words and no doubt refers to incidents that actually happened. A large number of bothy ballads about particular farms do this and many farms had someone who was a dab hand at rhyming and could produce such ditties when they all got together for a sing-song.

38. **Macfarlane o the Sprots**

This is one of the well-known cornkisters composed in the first half of this century by George Bruce Thomson of New Deer "to his ain tune" and appeared in *Folksong of the North-East* by Gavin Greig. It is a favourite song of Kate Halliday's who, of course, hails from the West of Scotland, so she does not sing it with so much of a North-East accent but with plenty of verve. It was one that she was asked to sing everywhere she went. She would dress up with tackety boots and an old cloth cap when she took part in Bothy Nichts and really captured the atmosphere of uninhibited fun that characterised these occasions. The lyrics demonstrate a vigorous and expressive use of doric and tell a cautionary tale of what happens if you're too shy to do your own courting.

39. **The Braes o Bonald** (or 'The Braes of Bonhill')

This song comes from an area in Dunbartonshire where the Old Kilpatrick Hills rise. The song is still known in that area. It was probably written in the latter part of the last century as an early music hall song and would be sold on a songsheet. While it belongs to the corpus of songs that express nostalgia for the old idyllic country ways, there is no sadness in it.

40. **Marnan Fair**

Marnan Fair took place at Aberchirder and although other villages like Dufftown adapted the song to their locality, this is the original. It is one of those rare broadside songs that actually celebrates happy married life. The fairs and markets of the North were not only places where men and women could get hired by farmers, but were also occasions for courtship. This song tells the story of such a courtship, in which the lad walks his lass "owre the heather", and takes her to a show in the evening, which, according to Jimmy MacGregor, would be a concert in the village hall at Foggieloan (the local name for Aberchirder). He buys her "candy in great lumps" which he kisses off her lips, and is later on taken home to meet her parents, who give their consent to the marriage. The song eventually celebrates the fact that they've "been blessed wi a pair o boys."

41. **The Pear Tree**

This song was learned by Dave Marshall about 1948 from a farmworker in a bothy at Westhaven. It was a very popular bothy ballad in Dundee and Sheena Wellington remembers Davy Glen singing it. It may have appeared on a songsheet from the Poet's Box, which was a source for many singers from both town and country. The change of person from "twa lads" to "we" in the song is not a mistake, but designed to add to the humour and impact of the song.

42. **The Beefcan Close**

Perhaps the most popular of all Dundee songs, it stands now as a commemoration of the Overgate, a street now replaced by a modern shopping centre. Described by Hamish Henderson as Dundee's Reeperbahn, it was a favourite haunt of country folk come to town for enjoyment of one sort or another and was the location of the Poet's Box where penny songsheets could be bought. In the early 1900s there actually was a Mrs Bruce who "kept a disorderly house", and one of her 'girls' was a Jemima Rose, so-called because of her red hair. No doubt the story told in the song happened many times in its crowded closes and pubs and the song has a Rabelaisian flavour that evokes something of the atmosphere of the place.

43   The Tradesman's Plooin Match

This entertaining bothy ballad, performed by Jock Duncan with plough-guiding actions in the chorus, was written by George Morris. Before the Second World War, there really was a Tradesman's Plooin Match at Old Meldrum, organised on Hogmanay, that allowed anyone who wasn't a ploughman to take part. The consequences must have been hilarious to the local horsemen! As Jock himself puts it, "There was nae muckle gweed work deen !" Ploughing matches were undertaken as serious tests of skill, but this unlikely one is more of a test of the ingenuity of the punning rhymster and the tongue-twisting prowess of the singer! Jock was once in Fyvie and was shown a medal by a local man who said his father won it at the Tradesman's Plooin Match many years before.

44.   The Dying Ploughboy

Also known as 'The Term', it appeared first in *Lilts o the Lea-Rig* by a "Herd Loon" (Rev. Robert H. Calder, minister of Glenlivet) published in Brechin in 1900. It was also reported by one of Greig's informants as having been composed in the New Aberdour district by a young man who died under the circumstances referred to in the song. The same account was given to the editor by the Lovie family of New Aberdour, who also pointed out the farm where it took place.

45.   The Rovin Ploughboy

The first verse of this song was learned by John MacDonald's father from a farm servant on the farm where he worked. John added the rest and it is reminiscent of 'The Gypsy Laddies' in the second verse. The theme of leaving everything to follow a lover is perfectly adapted to the rural scene, in which farm workers moved from farm to farm and the girl who fell in love with the ploughman could be faced with the choice of following him or losing him. In this case, she is willing to reject the advances of "the auld laird himsel" to throw in her lot with the ploughman. He has to be imagined, not as some rustic clodhopper, but as one of the "made horsemen" of the Horseman's Word, the secret society of ploughmen, who had power over horses and women in an age when, in the words of another song, "The ploomen laddies are aa the go".

46. Grat for Gruel

This comic song does not paint a very flattering picture of the weaver, but this may have been a fashion, as in another ditty that begins :-

> O mother, onybody! onybody!
>
> O mother onybody, ither than a weaver!

With the decline of hand-loom weaving, the reduced circumstances of the weaver might well give him little chance of the niceties of life and make him a creature, as described in the quoted rhyme, "o skin and bane", living on gruel. Tom Johnston, in his *History of the Working Classes in Scotland,* observes that the handloom weavers' income declined from thirty shillings a week in 1806 to only four shillings and fourpence a week in 1838. Ailie Munro and Hamish Henderson both identify an element of satire in the song, which sees greetin for gruel as a ruse to postpone going to bed. Indeed, older versions make it clear that the theme was not greed but impotence:-

> "And O," said the silly bridegroom
>
> "I kent this day wad come."

Willie MacKenzie gives the idea a practical twist: "It's the belly that keeps the back up".

47. Bonny Ythanside

This song, which appeared in Ord's collection, is one of the songs of rural courtship found all over Scotland that reflect a plainer way of life than that of the present day. We can work out from the song just what sort of behaviour was expected of young people in this situation: she must not be too forthcoming, but a smile was enough encouragement to walk her home; he had to show respect to her parents, be honest about his intentions and not outstay his welcome. He obviously passed the test!

48. Bogie's Bonny Bell (GD Vol 7)

Sung to the tune of 'The Plains of Waterloo', this song dates from 1865. Written by John Geddes, the grieve at Boghead of Cairnie, the farm in question, it is based on real events. It reflects an age when neither farm servants nor women had many rights. There are a large number of versions of this song in the *Greig-Duncan Folk-Song Collection*, which shows its continuing popularity. It is more lyrical and haunting than the usual type of bothy ballad. Tom Spiers' version and his singing of it are particularly fine.

49. Half Past Ten (GD Vol 7)

This song appears in Ford's *Vagabond Songs and Ballads of Scotland*, the Poet's Box, Glasgow Collection 1003 and in Ord. Gavin Greig wrote: "The above ditty is exceedingly popular. Although it is now in traditional keeping, I find it given in Harvey's *Harp of Stirlingshire* as the composition of a Mrs Bacon, who was born early last century, and who in 1897 was still alive and resident near Falkirk. She wrote other songs of merit, but none of these seems to have survived. Ford who gives 'Half Past Ten' in his *Vagabond Songs and Ballads* says it is sometimes sung to an adaptation of 'The Laird of Cockpen'. We have always got it to the tune which he himself prints".

50. Drumdelgie (GD Vol 3 No 384)

This is a classic bothy ballad whose tune is one of the most popular in North-East tradition. Gavin Greig wrote: "The large farm of three hundred acres was created at Drumdelgie in 1838. It was farmed from then till 1860 by William Grant and thereafter by his son, William, when it was enlarged to six hundred acres and the male workforce increased from eight to sixteen, which is beyond that indicated in any version of the song". The song gives a detailed picture of the working life of the farm servants, its unremitting toil in all weathers and the cheerful courage of the bothy chiels.

51. Granny Fraser's Flitting

This is a music hall song that is a comic epic with tongue-twisting lyrics, listing a catalogue of absurdities. This is well adapted for stage performance but can also suit the atmosphere of a ceilidh or a sing-song. Its popularity as a songsheet is easy to imagine. The tune as notated is the basis for the song but Ron Bisset performs it with bravura, varying tune and tempo freely to hilarious effect.

52. I'm No Comin Oot the Noo

This is a music hall song heard by Tommy Bonthrone at a concert party in Bathgate, and it became one of the standards of the Stewarts of Blair, who learned it from Tommy. Commenting on this song in his book *Till Doomsday in the Afternoon*, Ewan MacColl is of the opinion that an instalment of "half a crown a week" and the reference to lodgings full of fleas (to be treated with Keating's Powder) suggests the song belongs to the early years of this century. It came from the pen of James Curran, a noted Glasgow songwriter, whose songs appeared on songsheets sold at the Poet's Box in the Gallowgate. He was also responsible for 'The Soor Milk Cairt' and 'Fitba Crazy'.

53. The Auld Meal Mill

This is a sentimental song but a cut above the usual and is still a popular song among country people in Angus. Meal milling died out with the advent of mass production in factories of patent porridge mixtures, but the old buildings lingered on as landmarks and would be good places for lovers' trysts, as they usually stood on their own, away from the surrounding farms.

54. Princie and Jean

This song is something of a tear-jerker, but nevertheless, it is hard to resist when sung by Bothy Ballad King Tam Reid. The song was written by an Orcadian songwriter George Corigall and appeared in the *People's Journal* in 1960. It is sung to the modern tune of 'The Road and the Miles to Dundee'. When he mentioned in a radio interview with Robbie Shepherd that he would like to meet the author, not knowing that he was dead, Tam received a letter from George's sister Mrs Bella Mowat, and since then Tam and his wife have been regular visitors to Orkney. The song appeals to Tam because he understands from personal experience the great bond that existed between a ploughman and his horses.

55. Cock-a-Doodle-Doo

This is another song in the music-hall tradition, where humour was sometimes a bit rauch, but there has never been anything wrong with a good belly laugh now and then. It's the kind of comic song to be sung straight-faced or with an expression of outraged innocence when the audience laughs. George McWilliam sang the song with only two lines in the fourth verse.

56. The Laird o Tomintoul

Perhaps the forerunner of the comic Scot with the curly walking stick, the Laird is a hilarious figure, particularly as portrayed by Willie MacKenzie with his irresistible grin. There's something of the reckless panache of 'The Man that Broke the Bank at Monte Carlo' about it.

57. It's Aa Wan Tae Me

A song in music hall style, which reflects, nevertheless, a rural lifestyle and was popular in the bothies among the single men. Sandy Watt learned songs like these from his family and also among the country people both in the West and the East of Scotland at sing-songs and go-as-you-pleases. It works well as a children's song, with its formulaic repetition and its simple humour.

58. The Irish Boy

This version of the widespread song of the forsaken girl with its lines:-

> I wish, I wish, but I wish in vain,
> I wish I were a maid again,

was learned by Phyllis from her mother in Wigtonshire. The reference to Irish is often taken to mean Gaelic, but the proximity of the area to Ireland, the existence of a section of the population called Galloway Irish and the similarity of the Antrim dialect to Scots, make another interpretation possible. Three of the four verses of this song are "floating" verses that appear in many other songs of the same kind, but that in no way detracts from its lyrical beauty.

59. **Wha'll Mowe Me Noo?**

This is a bawdy song from Burns's *Merry Muses of Caledonia*, but one that also has a poignant quality. Its satire attacks the hypocrisy of the respectable women who condemn the prostitute, "mowin for its breid", while concealing their own moral lapses that come about through "glutton greed". A distinction has to be made between bawdy songs of this kind and smutty songs, based on two different attitudes to sexuality: the honest, down-to-earth and the dirty-minded. Gordeanna likes this song because it shows that Burns understood and sympathised with the woman's plight, and did not merely laugh at it.

60. **The Echo Mocks the Corncrake**

This Ayrshire song appears in Ford's *Vagabond Songs and Ballads of Scotland* and also in the Greig-Duncan Collection. Greig says of it: "It is not a true folksong but belongs to the class of what may be called 'composed' songs in the construction of which a certain amount of literary skill and device is exhibited". This distinction is not one that should matter much in Scotland, where the line between oral and literary tradition has been constantly blurred, by bookish tradition bearers and singing scholars. Ford said he had come across it on songsheets, so it seems to have been very popular. The sound of the corncrake used to be a familiar one in the Ayrshire countryside, but now it is hardly heard at all.

61. **The Belt wi Colours Three**

Alison McMorland learned this song from Lucy Stewart but sings it in a different style. A full transcription of her singing is contained in the special appendix at the end of the book and is included to provide an illustration of how a traditional singer can creatively mould a tune to fit the words, so that they are pointed to advantage. As Ailie Munro pointed out in *The Folk Music Revival in Scotland*, from which the transcription was taken, she was influenced by Lucy's cousin, old Davie Stewart's singing of 'The Dowie Dens of Yarrow.' It seems a very old song, to judge by the language and the strange symbolic imagery : a heavy leaden cap of sorrow, a black mantle for mourning and the sombre belt itself, putting a fatal stricture on the joy of young love. The metaphor of climbing a tree to herry a nest and falling down to the arms of a loved one is also found in No 66, Sheila Stewart's 'False, False'. Brian Miller has transcribed a simplified version of the tune from Alison's record of the same title.

62. **Tail Toddle**

This piece of mouth music to the tune of 'The Chevalier's Muster Roll' appears in the *Merry Muses of Caledonia* and was no doubt collected by Burns. Hamish Henderson has, on more than one occasion, sung this for dancers to do a reel. His version has a verse more than Burns', which is not surprising as this form lends itself to improvisation and there may be plenty more where that came from!

63. Dae Ye Mind Lang, Lang Syne?

This nostalgic song was written by a minister, the Rev. George S. Lawrie. Both the idiom of the song and the references to Winning Hill place it in Ayrshire. This may be a corruption of Whinnyhill or it could be associated with Coswinning Hill near Dalry. Its popularity no doubt sprang from its evocation of a rural childhood.

64. 'Twas Up Yon Dark and Stormy Glen

This is a variant of 'Skippin Barfit Thro the Heather' and 'The Queen Amang the Heather', a lyrical song of courtship with a happy ending. The romantic idea of a nobleman's son falling in love with a shepherd's daughter has been very popular in folk tradition and given rise to many similar songs cf. 'The Laird o Drum'.

65. The Band o Shearers (GD Vol 3 No 406)

This song is attributed to a nephew of James Hogg, who lived in the early 1800s, but Greig thinks it is older than that because so many widely differing versions of it, both oral and printed, existed when he was collecting. He would put it in the eighteenth century. It refers to the shearing of corn with heuks. Harvest time was always a good time for courtship as the men and women worked together in the fields. There are two different versions in Ord, 'The Gallant Shearers' and 'The Band o Shearers'.

66. False, False Hae Ye Been

This lovely lyric could be a fragment of a longer song but it stands very well on its own. The expressive jumps in the tune reinforce the passionate feeling behind the words and its language is full of the formulaic quality found in old ballads. The second verse echoes 'Johnnie Armstrang's :-

> Tae seek het water aneth cauld ice -
> Surely it is a great folie.

The third verse also reminds us of No 58 'The Irish Boy.' The song should be sung very freely and lends itself to decoration, although it is equally effective sung without.

67. Love and Freedom

This song by Mary Brooksbank has been sung and recorded a good deal in the last thirty years. You can tell it was written by someone with a cheerful outlook on life, a love of independence and a delight in music and dance. It appeared in her book *Sidlaw Breezes* which was published during her lifetime.

68. The Tamosher

This is a corruption of the word "stomacher", which was an article of clothing worn by women consisting of a stiff, sometimes embroidered, panel across the chest ending in a point over the stomach. The symbolism attached to it in the song clearly refers to pregnancy, to conceal which "she bundled it an rolled it in her apron," as wearing it would have made her condition plain to see. Going to pull rushes seems to have been a risky business for young girls both in Scots and French tradition!

69. The Rigs o Rye

Ord writes: "This fine old country song seems to have been missed by all the well-known collectors. I sent a copy to the late Robert Ford, but by the time it reached him, his *Vagabond Songs and Ballads of Scotland* were already in the press, so that he could not include it. The music was noted down by J. B. Allan, an organist in Glasgow from the singing of an Aberdeenshire ploughman". The tune seems to be related to that of No 4 'The Beggar Laddie'. It is an example of an old type of song in which the young man tests his sweetheart by pretending her family's opposition to him and her own lack of a fortune has put him off. When her tears start to fall, he relents and says, "I said it aa but tae try ye!" and they go off together "the hills an the valleys o'er." Probably, present day feminists would not think much of this kind of behaviour, but these things happened long ago and perhaps they still do.

70. My Last Farewell to Stirling

This is of the genre known as the transportation ballad which gives account of how men and women were condemned to be sent overseas as convicts for periods of perhaps twenty years to Van Diemen's Land and other penal colonies for offences such as petty theft or poaching. The latter seems to have been the case here as the song speaks about raising hares and pheasants on nocturnal ventures, and includes a request by the young man to his comrades to look after his dog and gun in his absence. There are few transportation ballads as lyrical as this one. The tune, according to Ewan MacColl, "seems to be adapted from a slow strathspey".

71. The Boys o Callieburn

This was an emigration song learned by Willie Scott from Willie Mitchell of Kintyre. There is a solemnity about the song which seems to express the finality of the goodbyes taken by men who never expected to see their homes and their loved ones again. The song is an indictment of inhuman, harsh historical changes such as the Highland Clearances.

72. The John McLean March

This great song by Hamish Henderson is a tribute to a Glasgow school teacher of Highland parentage, who became a convinced socialist and was one of the few working-class leaders in Western Europe who opposed the First World War from the start. He took his protest against the arms race to the shipyard gates, with the result that he was jailed for his anti-war activities. When he was released in December 1918, there was a tremendous turn-out of his supporters on Red Clydeside to welcome him back to the city. He is a revered figure among left-wing supporters and one with whose views many people are now in sympathy. I was told by American writer Archie Green that five men from Renfrew who were supporters of John McLean emigrated to San Francisco and there laid the foundations of the shipbuilding industry and the shipbuilders' trade union.

73. The Collier's Eight-Hour Day

The words are on a broadside published by Robert Macintosh, whose print shop was in Glasgow's Gallowgate. The author is noted on the leaflet as John Wilson, collier. This could refer to a poet from Dalry, Ayrshire, who was known as "Dalry" Wilson, a Burns imitator and author of 'The Dodger's Wedding', obviously inspired by Burns's *Jolly Beggars*. The miners were in the forefront of the struggle for an eight hour working day, at a time when (1880s and 90s) a fifty-four hour week was common even in the best workplaces. The text has been set to the traditional tune of 'The bonny lad that handles the plough' by Geordie McIntyre.

BIOGRAPHICAL NOTES

JOE AITKEN (44)

Joe Aitken was born in 1944 at Easter Camno Farm near Meigle, Perthshire, of Aberdeenshire parents. They travelled round Perthshire and Angus until he was 9 years old, when they moved to the berryfields of Muirhead of Logie near Kirriemuir. He started work there at the age of 15, and has been there ever since. He has worked with the Boys Brigade for 40 years and has also been a retained fireman for 25 years, being Officer in Charge at Kirriemuir for the last twelve. He has sung in concert parties and at OAP nights for many years and got involved with the TMSA when the Kinross Festival moved to Kirriemuir. Since then he has won cups for singing at Keith, Kirriemuir, Auchtermuchty and Strichen Festivals and has made a cassette with Springthyme Records called *If You've Never Been tae Kirrie*.

WILLIE BARCLAY (31)

Willie Barclay was born in 1906 near Auchterderran in Fife. His father was killed in the First World War, after which his mother lost her reason and he was boarded out to an aunt who already had a big family. He ran away from there and became a farm servant at Fiungarth in Perthshire, where he was very happy for a number of years and was treated like a member of the family. Although initially engaged to a housekeeper on another farm, he met and married someone else, a war widow with children, whose poor circumstances he took pity on. He moved north first to Peterculter, then to Castle o Fiddes, near Stonehaven, where he became cattleman. There was always a ceilidh in his house, for he loved singing. He even sang to his cattle - one of them, perhaps as a result, winning the Milk Record for Scotland. He retired to Scone and died in 1986. His daughter Barbara Findlay and her family have been involved for years in the TMSA.

WILLIE BEATTIE (1)

Born in Canonbie in 1917, Willie Beattie has been a forestry worker on the Buccleuch Estate all his life. He lives at Caulside, a row of crofts near Canonbie, and is an expert gardener as well as a champion traditional singer, particularly of Border ballads. He loves Border history and is a Common Riding enthusiast and composes songs about his own life and community. A spirited singer who evinces a strong sense of pride in his tradition, he has won cups on both sides of the Border, at Newcastleton and Rothbury festivals.

JACK BECK (65)

Jack Beck was born in Dunfermline in 1942 and on leaving school, he served his apprenticeship as a painter and decorator in his father's firm. When his time was out, he joined a skiffle group and, aiming to broaden his experience, he went south with some friends for six months, returning just as the Folk Revival was starting. He joined first the jazz club, then the Howff Folk Club in Dunfermline. There he heard singers like Willie Scott and Archie Fisher and began singing in a duo with Barbara Dickson. He never became a fully professional singer, although he had the chance to do so. Instead, Jack, who liked his work, took higher qualifications through night school and got married. He has been connected with clubs and sessions in Dunfermline ever since and sings with the group Heritage. He has been to parts of Europe and the States, both with the group and as a solo artist.

ANNIE BELL (7)

Annie Bell was born in Milnathort in 1916, daughter of a farmworker serving as a soldier. She lived there until she was 7 years old and then moved with her family to Glenfarg. She danced, whistled, diddled, sang and played mouth-organ and melodeon from an early age. She married a ploughman, who later worked among both sheep and cattle, and she was in domestic service on farms in Perthshire and the Borders. She speaks of hard work but also happy times: making music in cottar house ceilidhs and taking part in most of the TMSA's festivals, as guest, cup-winning competitor and adjudicator. She loves to sing Scots songs with good tunes and lyrics. She now lives in Blairgowrie, where she runs the local Arthritis Club. Although severely affected by the illness herself, she is still active as an entertainer.

RON BISSET (51)

Ron Bisset was born at the Cowden of Drumleuchie, Fife, in 1933. His father was a hill shepherd and his mother worked outby on the farm. He learned most of his songs from his parents, as they sang to their children on the long winter nights. He has sung in halls in Fife, Angus and Perthshire as a member of the Howe of Fife Bothy Boys. As a lad of 20, he sang in the St. Andrews Hall, Nairobi to the Scottish people in Kenya, when he was there with the Black Watch. Ron guested at Kinross Festival and TMSA ceilidhs.

TOMMY BONTHRONE (52)

Tommy Bonthrone was born into a musical family in the Mearns around 1910 but, being orphaned at an early age, he was sent to work for his keep on farms as a supposed mental defective. It was while he was working at Woodside of Marlee on the Blair-Oliphant Estate near Blairgowrie in the 1950s, that his case was reviewed and he was "certified sane", as he humorously put it. Unembittered by the injustice he had suffered, he continued as a paid farm worker until his death at Auchinblae in the late 70s. Singing and diddling were the great pleasures of his life and he was well-known around Strathmore, where he was the great rival of Davie Glen in the go-as-you-pleases. It was from Tommy that the Stewarts of Blair learned 'I'm No Comin Oot the Noo', a music-hall song he picked up from the singing of a Glasgow concert party he heard while he was working on a farm near Bathgate.

MARY BROOKSBANK (67)

Mary Brooksbank was born Mary Soutar in Aberdeen in 1897 and moved to Dundee when she was 8 years old, living first in the Pump Close, then in Blackness Road. She grew up in poverty and hardship and was shifting bobbins in Kiddie's Mill by the time she was 15, later becoming a jute spinner. She had an enquiring mind and, despite lack of schooling, she read widely, writing poems and songs, and became well-known as an agitator for better working conditions. She married in 1924 and was widowed in 1960. Maurice Fleming the writer encouraged her to go to Dundee Folk Club, where many young singers learned songs from her. She also played the fiddle, and a collection of her work was published under the title of *Sidlaw Breezes*. In 1982, another autobiographical book was published called *No Sae Lang Syne*. She took part in the TMSA's Blairgowrie Festival and was recorded by Maurice Fleming, Hamish Henderson and Pete Shepheard. She died in 1980.

DAISY CHAPMAN (47)

Daisy Chapman, who was born in Crovie by Gardenstown, spent her childhood in Buchan, and subsequently lived in George Street in Aberdeen. It was in 1965-6 that Peter Hall first met her when she was in her fifties and a widow, and in 1968 she took part in the Living Tradition Concert at Aberdeen Folk Festival. Thereafter, she was a guest at the TMSA's Blairgowrie and Kinross Festivals, where her warm and friendly personality made her a favourite with audiences. A heart attack put an end to her singing activities and she is now in residential care.

WILLIE CLARK (50)

Willie Clark was born in 1912 and grew up in the farming community of Morayshire and Banff. He won the Bothy Ballad Cup at Forres in 1938 and was well-known for years for his fine singing. He farmed at Dalhirach near Aberlour from the end of the Second World War until he died in 1988. His brother George, also a singer, is renowned for throwing the hammer at highland games. Willie sang at Keith Festival and made a cassette of songs including 'Drumdelgie'.

DICK COWAN (17)

Dick Cowan was born in Newcastleton in 1892 on the day of Copshawholm Fair. Copshawholm is the old name for Newcastleton, still used by local people, sometimes shortened to "The Holm". He served an apprenticeship as a tailor and always made his own suits. He learned his songs from his master and the people he worked with. When the First World War came, he was turned down for the army, but worked as a postman during the War, as well as tailoring. Then after the War, when hand tailoring was on the decline, he had a job in the local coal yard at Riccarton Junction till he retired, after which he had a light job with a local factory that made overalls. He sang in the community at Burns Nights and other social occasions such as the Traditional Music Festival at

Newcastleton, until he died in 1981. He said of his singing, "If God has gien ye a voice, ye should use it."

SHEILA DOUGLAS (60)

Sheila Douglas was born in Sowerby Bridge, Yorkshire in 1932, and came to Renfrew with her Ayrshire father, a marine engineer, and Yorkshire mother in 1937. Music of all kinds was always a part of her everyday life and has always delighted her, and both her sons are musicians. Schooled in Renfrew and Paisley, she graduated from Glasgow University in 1954 and taught English in Glasgow, then in Perth, where she settled with her husband Andrew in 1959. From the early 60s, she was actively involved in the Folk Revival: running Perth Folk Club from 1968-74, organising concerts, ceilidhs and festivals, in which she pioneered competitions for storytelling from 1973, editing the *Scottish Folk Directory* and singing all over the country in clubs and at festivals. She was involved with the TMSA from 1968 as singer, committee member, compère and adjudicator, serving first as Publicity Officer, then as Chairman. Now retired from teaching, she is a full-time writer, performer, lecturer and broadcaster.

JOCK DUNCAN (43)

Jock Duncan was born at Gellybrae, New Deer, Aberdeenshire in 1925, moving when he was three to South Faddenhill, where he grew up working on the farm and enjoying the music in the farm kitchen. He recalls all the different work of the farming year and the busy social life of the farming community - the characters and concert parties and customs like feet-washing - and he still speaks the rich Buchan dialect. The gramophone was popular in his day, especially for the records of George Morris and Willie Kemp. He served with the Gordons during the War, and since then has lived and worked in Pitlochry. Married with two sons, both pipers, he is an Honorary Member of the TMSA in which he has played an active part.

FRANK DUTHIE (34)

Frank Duthie was born in Peterhead in 1933, son of a fisherman and a gutting quine, but his parents would not let him go to sea. He worked for a while with a firm making concrete blocks, but then a job came up in the Fishery Office, and he worked in Buckie as a fishery officer till he retired. Married with a son and daughter, he lives in Findochty. He has many fascinating recollections of the fishing communities of the North-East, particularly of the drift net fishing and the role of the women, as well as a large repertoire of their songs. Many of these reflect the life and work of his parents' generation, describing how lines were prepared, how fishermen navigated by landmarks and how the fishgutters travelled to other ports to work. He speaks of the closeknit community ties that united the fisherfolk and the loyalty they showed to one another, helping those who fell on hard times and protecting widows and orphans. He has a particularly strong admiration for the fishermen's wives, who worked so hard and often suffered grievous losses.

JOHN EAGLESHAM (73)

John Eaglesham was born in Govan in 1938 when the shipyards were in full production. He was a Glasgow Council librarian for 37 years which gave him access to the folksong collections in the Mitchell Library. In his childhood, he heard all kinds of songs in his home - art songs, opera, spirituals, but no traditional Scots songs till the early days of the Revival. His favourite singers are the traditional ones and the inventive and humorous singer/songwriters like Matt McGinn, Ewan MacColl and Adam Macnaughtan. He was a founder member of both The Clutha and Stramash and was first involved with the TMSA through competitions.

PETER FAIRBAIRN (16)

Peter Fairbairn has lived in Hurlford near Kilmarnock, then in Dunlop and now in Kilmaurs. He began singing at Kilmarnock Folk Club and in 1975, he won the Grants Whisky Songwriting Cup at Girvan Festival. Third in the Men's Singing at Kinross in 1977, he won the Eck Harley Rosebowl for Bothy Ballad in 1978, and adjudicated the Men's Singing. He is now one of the team of people involved in the publication of *The Living Tradition* magazine. He is particularly known for singing songs from the South-West of Scotland, an area whose songs have not been much explored recently.

DENNIS FINDLAY (69)

Dennis Findlay was born in 1946 in Glasgow and was brought up in a mining village in Fife. His father played the accordion and there used to be ceilidhs in the house on Saturday nights with all kinds of songs being sung. He is married and has two sons and a daughter, all of whom are musical. When they moved to Forfar, he met singers like Charlie Murray and became interested in traditional singing. Charlie persuaded him to go to Auchtermuchty Festival where he met other singers like Tam Reid. He became involved in the TMSA as part of the Angus Branch and the Kirriemuir Festival Committee in the late 70s, and has guested at Auchtermuchty, Keith and Kirriemuir. He now lives in Glasgow as caretaker of Trades House, where very successful TMSA ceilidhs have been run.

RAY FISHER (36)

Ray Fisher was born in Glasgow but for many years has lived in Whitley Bay, Tyne and Wear, the home of her husband, musician Colin Ross. She has nevertheless retained every atom of her Scottishness and remains a firm favourite with Scottish audiences. One of the singing Fisher family, she made a name for herself in the early days of the Folk Revival with her brother Archie on the television programme *Hoot' nanny* and in the folk clubs. Her early singing style, like that of many young Revival singers, was American-influenced but this changed when she became a great admirer of Jeannie Robertson. She sings mostly with guitar and has sung and judged at TMSA festivals for many years.

GEORGE GALL (64)

George Gall was born in 1927 on a farm near Guildtown in Perthshire and went to school there and in Perth, leaving at 13 years of age. He moved to Logie Farm, Newburgh, Fife, and married in 1947. He had four children, two sons and two daughters, eleven grand children and three great-grand children, but never saw the latter as he died in 1989. His father knew a lot of old songs and played the accordion, as did his uncles. His wife's family also knew old songs and played the fiddle and accordion. When he was young, he sang at Harvest Homes and in pubs. He met Pete Shepheard in Largoward and was introduced to the folk club at the Star Hotel in St Andrews. He went to Blairgowrie Festivals, to Kinross Festival as a guest in 1970 and he also sang at the first Auchtermuchty Festival.

KATE HALLIDAY (38)

Kate Halliday was born in Rosneath on the Clyde, the daughter of a farm servant who worked mainly in Dunbartonshire and Ayrshire. In 1940, she came to Fife to Newton of Collessie, where the rest of her working life was spent. From here she took part in dances, Harvest Homes and concerts, and joined the Howe Bothy Boys and later the Lomond Cornkisters as "Collessie Kate". She won the Brose Caup and the prize for Best Female Entertainer of the Year on Grampian Television in 1970. Now she lives in retirement in the West of Scotland.

ECK HARLEY (37)

Eck Harley was born in the early 1900s and drove his first pair of horse on Kinninthmonth Farm, Ceres about 1926, for which he was paid eleven shillings for fifty hours' work. Then he went into the bothy, where he got his bed, coal and light and seventy pounds of oatmeal and salt per year, plus four pints of milk a day. He spent all of his working life as a ploughman when work was hard, hours were long and pay was small. He thinks modern mechanised farming makes life much easier. In the bothies, there was always music on the fiddle, penny whistle or mouth organ, plenty of songs round the bothy fire, and they used to dance in the middle of the road, when the maids from the farm might join them. Eck, who has an extensive repertoire of bothy ballads, has taken part in TMSA festivals for many years and is an Honorary Member.

HAMISH HENDERSON (62)

Hamish Henderson was born in Blairgowrie, Perthshire in 1919 and was educated at Dulwich College and Cambridge University. He served in North Africa and Italy with the 51st Highland Division in the Second World War. He then joined the newly-founded School of Scottish Studies in Edinburgh in 1951; he is an Honorary Fellow of the School, and has honorary doctorates from Dundee and Edinburgh Universities. An outstanding poet, singer and songwriter, he was a great pioneer of the Folk Song Revival, bringing together source singers and young Revivalists, and was President of the TMSA for several years. He has a great interest in and knowledge of both the Scots and Gaelic traditions and has been a major collector of songs and stories.

HEATHER HEYWOOD (21)

Heather Heywood was born in the mining village of Crosshouse, near Kilmarnock, Ayrshire in 1950, where her grandparents and their forebears were miners. Her father's family were from Port Glasgow and were descended from travelling people of the Gunn clan. She went to school locally, leaving at 15 years old to work in the local co-operative store. After she married Pete Heywood in 1970, she worked in a hosiery till she fell pregnant and now has three teenage daughters, the eldest being at Edinburgh University. She sang at family parties and at school from an early age with a repertoire of songs from mining disaster to music hall to Everley Brothers numbers. Pete introduced her to traditional songs and ballads, and singers like Martin Carthy influenced her. She was a founding member of Kilmarnock Traditional Folk Club and attended many TMSA festivals where she found more encouragement to sing unaccompanied than elsewhere. She has made two solo albums, *Some Kind of Love* and *By Yon Castle Waa* on the Greentrax label.

CATHY HIGGINS (28)

Cathy Higgins was born Cathy Stewart in Strabane in 1928, during the time her father's family spent in Ireland. Her father and mother were Alec and Belle Stewart and along with them and her sister Sheila, as the Stewarts of Blair, she has sung all over Britain and Europe. She married Jimmy Higgins, whose parents Jock and Charlotte were also tradition bearers. She has lived in Blairgowrie most of her life and has two sons and a daughter. She has her own repertoire of Scots and Irish song and a warm-hearted singing style.

LIZZIE HIGGINS (12)

Lizzie Higgins was born in 1929. Daughter of Jeannie Robertson and Donald Higgins, she grew up in the song, story and piping tradition. She lived for a while in Banchory during the war, doing occasional farmwork. In Aberdeen she worked at the fish gutting. As she developed, her singing style became markedly more decorated than her mother's; one important influence on her was her father Donald's virtuoso piping, but she was also influenced by English Revival singers who were aficianados of Irish *sean nos* singing. She sang in clubs and at festivals in Scotland and England, broadcast, was recorded and appeared on television. She was an Honorary Member of the TMSA and guested at its festivals. Lizzie died in Aberdeen in 1993.

JIMMY HUTCHISON (5)

Jimmy Hutchison was born in 1942 in South Uist in the Outer Hebrides. When he was 10 years old, he moved to Perth where he went to school and served his joinery apprenticeship. In 1960, he left Perth and worked in London for three years, where he went to the Singers' Club and heard singers like Ewan MacColl, Enoch Kent, Joe Heaney and Dominic Behan. His horizons were widened through acquaintanceship with Pete Shepheard with whom he visited County Clare, where he heard Irish singers at the *Fleadh Ceol* like Sean MacDonoghue and Michael Flynn. He came back to live in St. Andrews, where he sang at the Folk Club and was involved in the first Blairgowrie Festival and the Great Fife Road Show. He was the first winner of the Men's Singing Cup at Blairgowrie. Since then, he has lived in the Borders, Argyleshire and Fife. Alastair Clark of *The Scotsman* wrote of him, "He sings with craftsmanship and intensity that makes the nerves tingle."

ROBIN HUTCHISON (15)

Known as Blin Robin, Robin Hutchison was born in Peterhead in 1887 and died in Aberdeen in the late 1970s. He was one of a North-East family of the travelling people and was a guest at Kinross Festival. Hamish Henderson remembers him as a singer and piper and as one of the people who led him to Jeannie Robertson in 1953. Willie MacPhee remembers Robin and his son travelling in a motorbike and side-car and playing the accordion at highland games, and once gave them a lift from Braemar to Pitlochry. He was also known to the Stewarts of Blair. Robin guested at Aberdeen Folk Festival in 1968 and at the TMSA Festival at Kinross in 1975.

ARTHUR JOHNSTONE (72)

Arthur Johnstone was born in the house where he still lives in Knightswood, Glasgow, in 1941 on the day Germany invaded Russia, the 22nd of June. He left school at 15 and after working in a garage, served his time as a marine diesel fitter with Gleniffer Diesels in Anniesland. He has been a plant maintenance engineer with Strathclyde Buses for many years. There were always songs in the family, both his mother and father knew songs, but his own interest began with youth hostelling and camping weekends when he heard the protest songs of the time. Then he started going to folk clubs where he heard both Scottish and American singers and to festivals such as Irvine Marymass and the TMSA's Blairgowrie and Kinross Festivals, where he heard source singers. He started singing with the Laggan, who took their name from Loch Laggan where they often went camping. Winner of the Men's Singing Cup at Kinross, he also remembers the Scone ceilidhs and the singers he met and heard at them. Arthur ran the Star Folk Club in Glasgow for many years.

ROBERT LOVIE (14)

Robert Lovie was born on Green Park Farm, New Aberdour, and was noted as a singer at TMSA Festivals when he was only 13 years old. His grandfather, Gordon McQueen, was one of Gavin Greig's informants and wrote 'The Ardlaw Crew', one of the bothy ballads in the collection. Robert has won competitions, guested at festivals, broadcast, recorded and appeared on television and toured abroad.

JOCK LUNDIE (27)

Jock Lundie was born in 1907 at Blacklaws Farm near Blairgowrie, and he was a ploughman from the age of fifteen on a succession of Perthshire farms, eventually serving twenty years at Aberbothrie, from which he was reluctant to retire at 65. He can talk fascinatingly about the care and management of plough horses, for which he always had great patience and understanding. He was twice married, his first wife being killed in a road accident, and has an extensive family. He heard songs in the bothies from an early age and has a large and interesting repertoire. Now well into his eighties, he still sings, dances at ceilidhs and has a rich store of stories about horses and horsemanship. He has sung at Auchtermuchty Festival and is an Honorary Member of the TMSA.

JIMMY MACBEATH (46)

Jimmy MacBeath was born in Portsoy in 1894. He left school at 13 and was feed at St. Brandon's Fair to a farm in the parish of Deskford, where he was subjected to beating. Jimmy joined the Gordon Highlanders in 1914, serving in Flanders and Ireland. After he was demobbed, he became a street singer at the instigation of Geordie Stewart, a wealthy scrap dealer and brother of Lucy Stewart of Fetterangus. He became a well-known character, singing around the farm toons and at fairs and markets. He was discovered in 1951 by Alan Lomax and Hamish Henderson and subsequently sang at the People's Festival in Edinburgh and became a favourite singer in the Folk Revival, from whom many other singers learned songs. He lived in the model lodging house in East North Street in Aberdeen, where he was befriended by singer Peter Hall, and died in Tornadee Hospital on 7th January 1972.

JOHN MACDONALD (45)

John MacDonald, The Singing Molecatcher, was born at Bogney, Dunphail on 24th October, 1905 and died in Inverness on 21st January, 1987. He grew up on farms and became known as "the mowdie man" (the mole man) on the Pitgaveny Estate, where he lived for many years in a showman's trailer. A kenspeckle figure around the Elgin district, he collected melodeons and toured the country entertaining with songs, tunes, stories and conjuring tricks. He broadcast programmes about "slavery work", as he saw the toil of farmworkers in his father's day, and made a record called *The Singing Molecatcher*.

JIMMY MACGREGOR (40)

Jimmy Macgregor was born in 1922 in Garmouth, Morayshire and spent all his boyhood in the Laigh of Moray, where his father was a farm grieve. After attending Forres Academy, he worked as a gamekeeper and served in the Army, before joining the Kinross Police. Out of nostalgia, he began to collect and perform North-East songs, assisted by Sandy Davidson, the Botriphne Blacksmith, a prominent bothy ballad singer. He sang to foster good relations between the police and the public in various country areas where he worked, and on retiring from the police, he took to compering ceilidhs, concerts and fiddlers' rallies, and later commentating at agricultural shows, highland games and game fairs, which he is still doing. He has sung and won cups at TMSA festivals including Kinross, Keith and Kirriemuir.

WILLIE MACKENZIE (56)

Willie MacKenzie was born in 1923 at Kinnermony Farm near Aberlour, second of the five sons of a ploughman. His father later became a cattleman and worked on various farms. Willie worked first on a milk cart, then was a meal miller at Miltonduff for twenty six years, and after that he was a postman in and around Elgin. There were always ceilidhs in the house at Miltonduff. He learned songs from Jimmy McBeath and later joined the Elgin Folk Club in the days of the Revival. He married Freda in 1946 and they have both been active and keen supporters of the TMSA, particularly at Keith Festival, whose organisers in recent years have taken to featuring Willie on the festival tee-shirt. His cheerful singing style and distinctive foot-on-chair stance is known all over the North of Scotland.

ADAM MACNAUGHTAN (22)

Adam Macnaughtan was born in 1939 and in his childhood heard music-hall songs, Gilbert and Sullivan, 'Wide Wide as the Ocean', Robert Burns, Cole Porter, 'Maggie Cockabendie', 'The Toorie on his Bonnet', 'The Kerry Dances', Lionel Monkton, 'Imphm', 'The Darkies' Sunday School', 'The Bonny Wee Country Lass', Billy Cotton, Big Bill Campbell and his Rocky Mountain Boys, 'The Soor Milk Cairt' and 'Down at the Mains'. Adolescent musical experience took him through the school choir, Trad Jazz and Carntyne Old Church Operatic Club into skiffle, Tom Lehrer and Flanders and Swann. In the late Fifties, he joined the Glasgow Folk Song Club and was a founder member of the Glasgow University Folk Song Club. As an unaccompanied singer his interest quickly swung from skiffle to Scottish songs, particularly local Glasgow material; as a school teacher, he became interested in children's traditions. When he stopped full-time teaching in 1980, he devoted his time to researching the Glasgow broadside publishers.

WILLIE MACPHEE (29)

Willie MacPhee was born in 1910 and is probably one of the last of the travelling tinsmiths, still retaining his tools and his skills, although there is little call for them nowadays. His aunt married old John Stewart, father of the late Alec Stewart of Blairgowrie. He lives with his equally remarkable wife Bella in a comfortable trailer on the Doubledykes site at Inveralmond, near Perth. A jack-of-all-trades from making willow baskets to mending old engines, he has travelled all over Scotland and Ireland and used to play his pipes along with his cousin Alec Stewart in Glencoe and other beauty spots. A piper, singer and storyteller, he has been used all his life to ceilidhing and enjoys going to clubs and festivals. He taught himself to read pipe music and has a repertoire of very old traditional tales as well as many good songs. He is one of the founder members of the Scottish Storytelling Forum and a member of the Guid Crack Company.

DAVE MARSHALL (41)

Dave Marshall was born in 1932 on a farm near Carnoustie and started in the bothy as a horseman, later becoming a tractorman. In the 70s, he worked on a farm near Coupar Angus. He was well-known in the diddling competitions in rural Angus and Perthshire and also plays mouth organ, melodeon and sings bothy ballads. He was a guest at Blairgowrie Festival in 1968 and Kinross Festival in 1976.

PHYLLIS MARTIN (58)

Phyllis Martin was born in Garlieston, Wigtonshire in 1944, leaving there when she was 15 years old to attend Logan and Johnston Pre-Nursing College in Glasgow, and later working in Kilmarnock Infirmary. In 1963, she married and moved to Somerset and then to Kent, returning to Scotland in 1970, when she became involved in folk music. Her father Walter and mother Joan both sang. 'The Irish Boy' was a song her mother had learned from Phyllis's grandmother Annie Mary McCrae. Phyllis has sung in and won competitions at TMSA festivals since the 1970s and now sings with the women's a cappella group Stravaig.

GORDEANNA McCULLOCH (59)

Gordeanna McCulloch was born in 1946 in Bellshill and grew up at Farme Cross in Rutherglen. While a pupil at Rutherglen Academy, she was a member of Norman Buchan's School Ballads Club, singing mainly traditional songs from the age of 16. By the time she was 18, she was with The Clutha and sang with them for over 20 years. She was married in 1968 and won the Women's Singing Cup at Kinross in the 1970s. During her years with The Clutha she made four records, including the solo album *Sheath and Knife*. After The Clutha disbanded, she sang solo, then together with Chris Miles she joined up with Aileen Carr and Maureen Jelks as Palaver. Gordeanna attended TMSA festivals at Kinross, Keith, Kirriemuir and Auchtermuchty, but only became a member after the formation of the Glasgow Branch, which she later chaired. She has subsequently become a National Committee member and was Chairman for a year.

DAVE McFADZEAN (18)

Dave McFadzean was brought up in the Upper Nithsdale mining community of Kirkconnel. When his father had a bad mining accident, the family moved to Thornhill further down the Nith valley. Dave has lived there ever since and would not be happy anywhere else. His first introduction to folk music was through hearing groups like the Corries, Gaberlunzie and The Spinners. Later, when he started going to Dumfries Folk Club, he found that there was a whole world of folk music he did not know about. On becoming a resident singer there, he started going to festivals and taking part in competitions, in which he was a frequent winner, and these are now his main pastimes. He attends about a dozen festivals every year and finds them a great help in learning songs. He has recently developed an interest in and a talent for storytelling and songwriting.

ALISON McMORLAND (61)

Alison McMorland was born in Clarkston, Renfrewshire, in 1940, of Ayrshire stock who were all musicians and singers. After primary schooling at Strathaven, she moved to England where she later trained as a drama/art teacher. She became involved in the Folk Revival in Cornwall and won the Women's Singing Cup at Kinross in 1971. Her main influences were Lucy Stewart of Fetterangus and Hamish Henderson. Since then, she has pioneered voice workshops for women and children, undertaken field collecting of songs, stories and lore, and made the award-winning *Pass It On* film in 1974 in Yorkshire. She guested at the U.S. Centenniel Celebrations in Washington, edited and compiled books of children's lore, such as *The Funny Family* and *Brown Bread and Butter* for Ward Lock, and *Herd Laddie of the Glen*, the songs and life of the late Willie Scott. She sang with the Albion Band and has done theatre work, made records, including *Belt wi' Colours Three*, and appeared on radio and TV. Now Glasgow-based, she works all over Britain as a free-lance community artist, initiating oral history and reminiscence projects. Her long-standing concern is with the traditional arts in the community as opposed to the folk club circuit.

GEORGE McWILLIAM (55)

George McWilliam was born in Dufftown on Glencorrie Farm in 1913 and worked on farms till he was 22, when he became a male nurse in West House Hospital, Edinburgh. In 1938, he was employed on the trams in Edinburgh and conscripted into the King's Own Scottish Borderers in 1940. After demob in 1946, he drove buses in Edinburgh for two years. Subsequently he became an inspector, later senior inspector, in the SSPCA, for three years in Linlithgow, seven years in Castle Douglas, followed by twenty years in Elgin, where he lived in retirement till his death in the 1980s. He won the Bothy Ballad Cup at Keith in 1979 and was a guest at Kinross Festival in 1980.

ALLAN MORRIS (4)

Allan Morris was born in 1941 and raised in Rutherglen where he attended the Academy from 1953-9, being taught by the late Norman Buchan. Married with one son, he has lived in East Kilbride since 1965. He took a B.A. (Hons) at Strathclyde in 1973 and teaches English. Founder and organiser of the Forum Folk Club in East Kilbride from 1968-73, Allan has won traditional singing cups at Kinross and Irvine festivals in 1973 and adjudicated and guested at Kinross in 1977 and 1978. He has also taken part in the late Arthur Argo's radio programmes, such as Folk Routes, during the 1970s and appears on two Scotsoun cassettes, *The Folk Music Revival in Scotland* and *Singers singing tae Sangsters.*

CHARLIE MURRAY (70)

Charlie Murray was born in 1916 in the Black Isle, the youngest of a family of ten, his father being a cattleman who moved from farm to farm. He was first feed at Nether Dallochy and got married in 1936. He heard Jimmy McBeath sing at the feeing markets in the 30s. With seven of a family, whose excellent upbringing he attributed entirely to his wife, he rose to the top of his profession and after a spell in the Lothians among the shorthorn cattle, he worked eventually at the Boots' Estate at Craigeassie near Forfar, where he became head cattleman breeding pedigree Aberdeen Angus champions. It was in these days that he first had leisure to sing in the Inn at Justinhaugh and came to the notice of the TMSA, thereafter winning cups, guesting and judging at festivals, and being made an Honorary Member. He died in 1991.

ANNE NEILSON (3)

Anne Neilson was born in 1944 and grew up in Rutherglen where she attended the Academy, being taught there by the late Norman Buchan, who started a folk club in the school where all kinds of songs were sung. She first sang with the Ian Davison Folk Group, and later became one of Stramash. She teaches English in East Kilbride. Her favourite songs are the North-East ballads and she has been active in the TMSA since the formation of the Glasgow branch. She took the Chair on the National Committee in 1993.

JOE RAE (2)

Joe Rae was born in 1937 on a farm between Darvel and Strathaven, the third child of a family of seven, his father being a ploughman. His family moved to Ayrshire where they lived at Sornhill, the March House and Mauchline, where he became an apprentice in a country joiner's shop after he left school. Following his marriage, he lived with his family at Sorn, then moved up to Bigholm near Beith. He worked in a Glasgow office for twenty years and thus "missed the chipboard era", then bought a joiner's business in Kilmacolm, where he works with his three sons, doing mainly craftsman joinery work. He has supported the TMSA for many years, competing in singing and storytelling competitions and has taken part in the Scottish Storytelling Festival at the Netherbow Arts Centre in Edinburgh.

JIM REID (30)

Jim Reid was born in Dundee and sang with the group called The Taysiders in the 1960s. A past Chairman and Honorary Member of the TMSA, he has been involved with festivals at Blairgowrie, Kinross, Keith, Kirriemuir and Auchtermuchty. A founder member of the famed Foundry Bar Band, playing guitar, mouthie and bagpipes, he has always been respected as a solo singer and songwriter. Recently, he has sung in a duo with accordionist Yvonne McLeod as Greylag. His album *I Saw The Wild Geese Flee* was a best seller and he has also recorded with musician John Huband. He has put tunes to the work of Angus poets, Violet Jacob and Helen B. Cruikshank. He worked at one time as a maintenance man in a lemonade factory in Arbroath, but since then has mainly worked in agriculture.

TAM REID (54)

Tam Reid of Echt was born in 1929. He won the title of Bothy Ballad King at Turriff in 1979 and is an Honorary Member of the TMSA. Tam, with his wife Ann, is a regular at all its festivals. He grew up in a farming family and still lives in his family home, having retired from a milk business he and his wife ran for 15 years. They are now launching a working museum and tearoom at the farm at Woodside, Cullerlie, with the huge collection of farm implements and machinery they have accumulated over the years. Tam is a walking encyclopaedia of old farming practices, which he can also demonstrate. They also hold bothy nichts with local singers and musicians. He likes to visit Orkney every year.

IRENE RIGGS (24)

Irene Riggs was born in Kirkcaldy, Fife, in 1948. Her mother claims she was "aye singing" and has never shut up since! Coming from a family with strong connections with the Salvation Army, Irene started singing with "The Army" as a child. Through hearing a recording made by Alex Campbell in the 1960s, Irene immediately became a devotee of Scots traditional music. She served as Secretary of the TMSA from 1976 to 1985. 'The Collier Laddie' is probably her favourite song, because as she says, "My father, both my grandfathers and my great-grandfathers were all coal miners. I have a great sense of pride in the culture and folklore of the miners. My father worked at what was said to be the oldest working pit in Scotland - the Frances Colliery in Dysart, Fife. Now that has gone the way of most pits - closed - but the sense of pride in a mining community is still there in former mining villages". Irene now teaches in a secondary school in Fife.

BOBBY ROBB (19)

Bobby Robb was born in Toronto of Scots parents who returned home when he was three. Apart from a short spell in Glasgow, he was schooled in Ayrshire where his father worked as a miner. Bobby worked in the boatyard when he left school, but eventually entered the building trade. He got married to Nancy McLean when he was 24 and they had seven children, most of whom became involved, like Bobby and Nancy, in the Folk Revival, about which he speaks with great enthusiasm. Girvan Folk Club and Festival owe a good deal to the Robb family. Bobby's repertoire has been acquired largely through the Revival, although his singing style is like that of the older singers.

JEANNIE ROBERTSON (11)

Born in Aberdeen in 1908, Jeannie was related to the Perthshire Stewarts through her mother and was discovered by Hamish Henderson in Aberdeen in 1953, when he was on a song-collecting trip in the North-East. She sang at Hamish's People's Festival Ceilidh in Edinburgh and, thereafter, at TMSA festivals in Blairgowrie and at Keele Festival in England, as well as in Scottish and English folk clubs. She became a recording and broadcasting artist, noted for her singing of the big ballads and telling traditional tales, and she was sought after by folklorists and collectors from all over the world. In 1968, she received the MBE in recognition of her services to folk tradition and she died in 1975.

STANLEY ROBERTSON (33)

Stanley Robertson was born in Aberdeen in 1940. His mother Elizabeth McDonald was a fine singer, his father William Robertson, a piper and his grandfather Joseph McDonald a great storyteller. His aunt was Jeannie Robertson, from whom he also learned songs. From the age of 14, he worked in the fish trade as a gutter and smoker, and has recently written books of stories called *Fish Hooses 1, 2* and *3*, as well as four other books, *Exodus to Alford, Nyakim's Windows, The Land of No Death* and *Ghoulies and Ghosties,* which are partly traditional story, partly his own creation. He is regarded as one of the foremost storytellers in Scotland. He was first encouraged to sing by his cousin Lizzie Higgins in 1960 and has been singing in clubs and at festivals ever since, winning cups for singing and storytelling, visiting schools and libraries and performing and lecturing abroad. Married with six of a family, most of whom also sing, he is a member of the Mormon faith and has visited America and Canada.

ANGUS RUSSELL (20)

Angus Russell was born in Kirriemuir in 1919, his real name being Rex, but taking the name Angus from his home county. He served in the Royal Scots Fusiliers in the Second World War and was commended for gallantry. A graduate of Glasgow University, he lived in Kilwinning and became an English teacher. He was involved in the Folk Revival from its earliest days - at the ceilidhs in Glen Doll and in Scone, as well as in the early folk clubs as a singer and storyteller. He was for many years a weel-kent face in folk clubs and at festivals all over Scotland and England. A member of the TMSA for many years, he also served on its Committee as well as on that of Newcastleton Festival. He went to live in Newcastleton and died in hospital in Carlisle in 1986.

WILLIE SCOTT (71)

Willie Scott was born in 1897 in the parish of Canonbie into a family of shepherds and traditional singers. He worked first when he was 11 years old at Stobbs near Hawick, and at 16 with his father in Teviotdale. Willie married Frances Thomson, a ploughman's daughter, in 1916 and they had six children. He loved the Common Ridings and the Herds' Suppers and, with Frances, was foremost in the musical life of Liddesdale. His work took him to many remote spots, where people had to make their own entertainment, and where there were few houses without a fiddle or two. When he was herding in Fife in the late 50s, he used to go to the Howff Folk Club in Dunfermline. A stalwart of the TMSA from its earliest days, he became one of its first Honorary Members and was a mainstay of the Newcastleton Festival. He died in 1989 at the age of 92.

ROBBIE SHEPHERD (49)

Born in Dunecht in Strathdon, Aberdeenshire, Robbie Shepherd has always been interested in folk songs and the music of the North-East. He started singing bothy ballads in his teens off the records of Willie Kemp, George Morris and Harry Gordon. Then he got a copy of Ord's *Bothy Songs and Ballads* and in his own words, "That was me away." Encouraged by the late Arthur Argo, he joined BBC Aberdeen in its early days, becoming a popular and well-known presenter and broadcaster on both radio and television . He gives the TMSA regular support by compering at ceilidhs and festivals.

MABEL SKELTON (8)

Mabel Skelton was born in Arbroath and learned many songs from her grandmother and mother. She married young and was widowed at 22 with two young children. She worked as a servant lass on the farm of Peasiehill, then later became a cook for many years at the army camp at Barry. She married Graham Skelton and had several more children. They lived courageously through many hard times, but she was always cheerful and saw the funny side of things. She had a tremendous love of Scots song tradition, which she tried to hand on to her family, and even when some of them emigrated to Canada, she regularly sent tapes of songs and stories to them, to play to exiled Scots there. She was introduced to the TMSA in the 1970s, appearing at Kirriemuir Festival and was recorded by Hamish Henderson before she died in the 1980s.

TOM SPIERS (48)

Tom Spiers was born in Aberdeen in 1947 and went to school at Powis, leaving at fourteen to go to Commercial College, which he gave up after a year to work at Stoneywood Paper Mill. He worked there for 18 years, attending day-release classes to learn paper-making. In his early thirties, he went first to England then to the Stirling area, where he became technical manager of the paper mill at Denny, moving back to Aberdeen as production manager of Donside Paper Mill. He played the fiddle from an early age, being tutored by Bert Murray at the Powis Community Centre when he was in Primary School, but gave it up in his teens, because he didn't like the classical music being taught at school. A workmate at Donside Mill was a founder of Aberdeen Folk Club and took him along there. At first he played his fiddle, until Arthur Argo encouraged him to start singing as well and introduced him to the material available from the Folk Club's library. Peter Hall, with whom he has performed in the Gaugers ever since their formation in 1965, has been a strong influence and has generously provided him with material from the *Greig-Duncan Folk-Song Collection.*

BELLE STEWART (6)

Belle Stewart was born as Belle Macgregor in a tent near Caputh in 1906, and raised in Blairgowrie. She has become world famous as a tradition bearer of the travelling people and was awarded the BEM for services to Scottish folk music in 1986. She was married in Ballymoney in County Antrim in 1925 and had two sons and three daughters, the youngest adopted. Discovered in the early 1950s by Maurice Fleming, she and her family were extensively recorded by Hamish Henderson for the School of Scottish Studies and appeared at the first Blairgowrie Festival in 1966, after which the TMSA was formed. As one of the Stewarts of Blair, along with her late husband Alec and daughters Sheila and Cathy, she has sung all over Britain, Europe and the United States. Her repertoire includes ancient ballads, broadsides, bothy ballads, music hall songs, Irish songs and her own songs, such as 'The Berryfields of Blair' and 'Whistlin at the Ploo'.

DAVEY STEWART (23)

Davey Stewart, a native of St. Andrews, was born in Dundee in 1946. Educated at Madras College and Strathclyde University and employed as a social worker in Fife, he is married with two children. Activities have included singing in St. Andrews Folk Club from 1963 and involvement with the TMSA from the first Blairgowrie Festival in 1966. In addition, he was President of the Strathclyde University Folk Club in 1968-70 and Chairman of the TMSA from 1968-70. He sang first with a folk group called the Down and Outs with Davey Craig, Brian Miller, Cilla Fisher and Artie Trezise, then from 1972 onward with John Watt. Their record *Shores of the Forth* was a best-seller in the British Folk Charts for two years. Davey's repertoire is mainly traditional, including comic songs and parodies, and concerned with the strength of the human spirit in the face of the trials and tribulations of life.

DAVIE STEWART (25)

A cousin of the Blairgowrie Stewarts, Davie Stewart, who was known by the nickname of the Auld Galoot, was born in Aberdeenshire in 1901. He tried to join the Gordon Highlanders at the age of 13, was pulled out by his father, but succeeded in getting back in and was wounded three times in the First World War. After the War, he and Jimmy MacBeath became companions and sang at fairs and markets. A piper from his army days, he later took up the accordion and melodeon, and travelled in Ireland for 20 years before returning to Scotland with his Irish wife Molly in 1950. He was recorded for the School of Scottish Studies in 1953 by Hamish Henderson and Frank Vallee. Hamish first saw him in Dundee busking for a cinema queue. Later, he was filmed by Peter Kennedy. He settled in Glasgow and was drawn into the Glasgow Folk Centre by its organiser Andrew Moyes. He died in 1972 on a visit to St. Andrews Folk Club.

ELIZABETH STEWART (13)

Elizabeth Stewart was born in Fetterangus, grand-daughter of Donald Stewart of Crichie. Her mother was the youngest and her famous Aunt Lucy, the eldest among the sisters of their family. Lucy stayed at home and kept house while the younger members of the family went out to work, so Elizabeth and her sister were brought up largely by Lucy and learned her songs. Elizabeth, like her mother, plays accordion, and also piano in a variety of styles, but above all, she has a passion for ballad singing. She was invited to the United States in the Fifties and has since revisited on a singing trip. She has also made a cassette of ballads and songs. In recent years, she has taken part in TMSA festivals and won several Women's Singing Competitions.

SHEILA STEWART (66)

Sheila Stewart was born in Blairgowrie in 1934, second daughter of Belle and the late Alec Stewart. She has lived in Blairgowrie all her life and grew up to inherit the song and story traditions of her family, with whom she has toured Britain, Europe and the United States. Her full-throated voice is ideally suited to tragic ballads and love songs. She has two sons, both pipers, and a daughter and several grandchildren. Sheila has sung at many TMSA festivals and taken part in the Scottish Storytelling Festival at the Netherbow Arts Centre in Edinburgh. She has also recently started doing voice workshops.

ANDY STIRLING (32)

Andy Stirling was born in 1918 in the Gorbals in Glasgow. After his mother died when he was 6 years old, he was boarded out to a lady in Aberdeenshire on a croft at the Hill of Longhaven, and actually attended school at Whitehills, where Gavin Greig was schoolmaster. It was from his foster-mother that he learned songs, and when he went to work on farms, he picked up bothy ballads. He returned to work in Glasgow, but later worked at the sawmill in Carrbridge. He became involved in the TMSA and guested at Kinross in 1979. He died a few years later.

CAMERON TURRIFF (10)

Cameron Turriff was born in 1911 in Crimond, the son of a cattleman from a family of farm servants, many of whom sang. Having always suffered with poor eyesight, he eventually became blind as his mother had done. He learned his songs from an early age from his mother, and in his working life from family and friends at meal-and-ales and other country festivities. As well as singing, Cameron told lively and vivid stories. He married Jane in 1957 and they lived in Gaval Street, Fetterangus, from which they travelled to take part in festivals, in spite of their physical handicaps. Festival-goers at Blairgowrie and Kinross in the 1960s and 1970s will remember their tireless and irrepressible enthusiasm for the old songs and how they loved entertaining their audience. Cameron died in 1973.

JANE TURRIFF (9)

Born Jane Stewart in Fetterangus in 1915, Jane Turriff now lives in Mintlaw, and is a cousin of the Perthshire Stewarts. She has inherited her family's musical talent and, since she had an accident at an early age, she has spent nearly a lifetime on crutches. It is hard to think of her as disabled, however, as she kept house for her parents and sisters, later marrying and raising her own family. Her favourite singers when she was growing up were Gracie Fields and Jimmy Rodgers, whose records she treasured and who influenced her singing style, which is clear-voiced, whole-hearted and tuneful. As singing is her greatest pleasure in life, she loves to go and "cheer up the old folk" in her own locality. She also has the rich tradition of the travelling people, who have done so much to keep the joy and beauty of Scots singing alive. She and her late husband Cameron sang at many TMSA festivals.

ANNIE WATKINS (42)

Annie Watkins was born in Dundee during the First World War, about 1916, and lived in Dundee all her life. She had always been a singer but was first recorded by Maurice Fleming in the late 1950s. Well-known as a local character, she came into prominence outwith Dundee in 1984 with the publication of *The Songs and Ballads of Dundee*, compiled by Nigel Gatherer and published by John Donald. She sang at the Coorse and Fine Concerts held in Dundee and Glasgow in 1985, 1986 and 1987 to launch the cassette which accompanied the book, and was noted for her version of 'The Beefcan Close'. She appeared at Kirriemuir Festival in 1986 and in Edinburgh. Virtually unable to read and write, she nevertheless composed songs and at ceilidhs could be seen enthusiastically joining in every song that was sung. In the closing days of her life in Roxburgh House in Dundee, she was given a concert by Jim Reid, Maureen Jelks and the Foundry Bar Band. Her only known relative was a sister in Australia.

JOHN WATT (26)

John Watt was born in Dunfermline, Fife, in 1933 into a family with a musical background on his father's side, although the household itself was not musical. By the age of 26, John had a great interest in jazz and sang in a skiffle group. In 1960, two friends introduced him to the Howff Folk Club in Edinburgh. He was hooked from then on, and started the Dunfermline Howff in 1961, where Willie Scott and his sons used to sing, as well as many other traditional singers like Jimmy McBeath and old Davie Stewart, who strongly influenced John. He started writing songs, some of which have been recorded by other artists, and sang for 8 years with Davey Stewart from the St. Andrews Folk Club, performing mainly Fife-based material, as featured on the Springthyme record *Shores of the Forth*. In 1965, he was Organiser/Chairman of the Federation of Scottish Folk Clubs and became involved in the TMSA after the Blairgowrie Festival of 1966. He later became Publicity Officer, then Chairman and helped to organise the first Kinross Festival.

SANDY WATT (57)

Sandy Watt was born in 1907 on a farm near Burntisland, moving with his family round several Fife farms till his father, a dairyman, went back to his home area of Carstairs, before returning to Fife yet again. Sandy went into service near Carstairs, cycling to Girvan every weekend where his father was then living. Then his father bought a bus and Sandy drove it for over twenty years until a crash put an end to the business. He married a miner's daughter and had three of a family. His favourite leisure pursuit was always going to sing-songs or go-as-you-pleases. When he was a milkman in Glenfarg, the Folk Club started there and he became a favourite singer, still being commemorated with a Quaich awarded annually in a singing competition. His repertoire included Child ballads, traditional songs, old music-hall songs, Irish songs, love songs, bawdy ballads and "wee ditties" learned from his mother.

JANET WEATHERSTON (63)

Janet Weatherston was born in 1947 at East Craigie Farm on the Dalmeny Estate on the outskirts of Edinburgh and was schooled in Dalmeny Village and South Queensferry in West Lothian. She spent much time with her grandmother in Kirriemuir, enjoying and learning songs. Records were becoming available, but the songs on them were not like those sung by her family and so she would pester the singers until she could get the words written down. She was content to sing the songs at family gatherings, and did not consider public performance until her brother John and his friend Norman Stewart, who was working on the estate at the time, took her to Edinburgh Folk Club. She found this therapeutic after her marriage broke up and since then she has sung at TMSA festivals and in folk clubs.

JOCK WEATHERSTON (35)

Like his sister Janet, he went to school in Dalmeny Village and in South Queensferry. They had the same up-bringing except that "he never did housework", according to Janet. At an early age, he was able to perform at family gatherings, weddings and Hogmanay celebrations. On leaving school, he was apprenticed to a large engineering works as a blacksmith welder. After his apprenticeship, he was keen to take on farm work and was employed by the same laird as his father. Then he decided to spread his wings and was bothied on a farm near Strathmiglo in Fife, and later near Blairgowrie. As his sister Janet reported, "On an evening's enjoyment near the farm, he was encouraged to sing and 'Brose aa Day' was well sung by the bothy lad." He returned to East Craigie and that led to his going to Edinburgh Folk Club with Norman Stewart. After that, he sang regularly at folk clubs, ceilidhs and festivals.

TOM WEBSTER (39)

Tom Webster was born in a farm cottage at Cuthil Tower, near Milnathort, one of a family of eight. He went to school in Milnathort and Kinross, worked in a grocery for six months before serving his time as a gardener, but later became a postman. He showed an early talent for singing, whistling and yodelling, first in the Boys Brigade, then in the Young Farmers and the Army, and after that, he joined the Bill Wilkie Show in Perth. From there, he went into the Andy Morris Show and later joined the Fife Yokels.

Appearances on Grampian Television's Bothy Nichts resulted in his twice winning the Male Entertainer of the Year Award. In 1970, he founded The Lomond Cornkisters and recorded for Grampian Records and Ross Records. He also performed and judged at the Kinross Festival. He has travelled to England and the Continent and, even though retired from the postal service, still pursues a punishing schedule of ceilidhs and concerts.

BETSY WHYTE (68)

Betsy Whyte was born in 1919 near Blairgowrie in Perthshire, where her family were tent-dwelling travellers. Her childhood and growing-up experiences are described in *The Yellow on the Broom* (1979) and the posthumous *Red Rowans and Wild Honey* (1990). In 1939, she married Bryce Whyte and settled in Montrose. A gifted storyteller and ballad singer, and a woman of great perceptiveness, she was recorded by the School of Scottish Studies, made a number of television appearances and was always a favourite at TMSA festivals. Her sudden tragic death at Auchtermuchty Festival in 1988 was a stunning blow.

ADAM YOUNG (53)

Adam Young was an old Angus bothy chiel who came to TMSA festivals with Charlie Murray and was famed for his comic renderings of bothy ballads. Like Charlie, he took part in the sing-songs in the Justinhaugh Inn. In his memorable version of 'The Three Craws', (which went on *ad infinitum*), the fourth craw "was drunk at Justinhaugh". He had memories of the old farming ways and of life in the bothy. He guested at Kinross Festival in 1972 and 1973. When he was living in retirement in Forfar, he used to attend the ceilidhs at Kirriemuir.

APPENDIX FACSIMILE*

Alison McMorland: *The belt wi' colours three*
Kinross 1975; rec. A.P.   AM26.

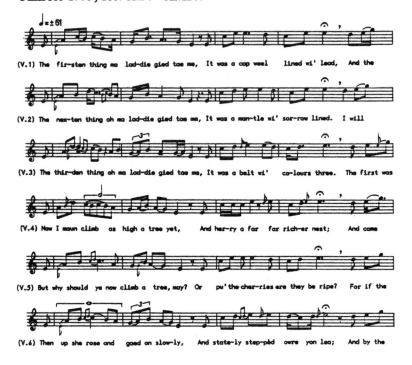

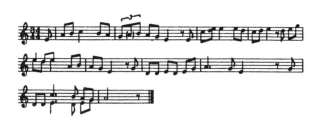

*This is taken from Ailie Munro's book *The Folk Music Revival in Scotland* (pages 114–5). A simplified form of the melody can be seen above and the material at the foot of the following page is cited by the author as influencing Alison McMorland's setting. (See note to song no. 61 on page 139)

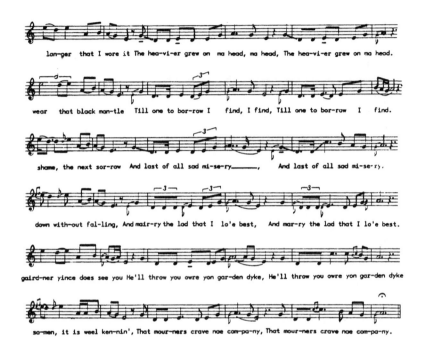

lon-ger that I wore it The hea-vi-er grew on ma head, ma head, The hea-vi-er grew on ma head.

wear that black man-tle Till one to bor-row I find, I find, Till one to bor-row I find.

shame, the next sor-row And last of all sad mi-se-ry_____, And last of all sad mi-se-ry.

down with-out fal-ling, And mair-ry the lad that I lo'e best, And mar-ry the lad that I lo'e best.

gaird-ner yince does see you He'll throw you owre yon gar-den dyke, He'll throw you owre yon gar-den dyke

sa-men, it is weel ken-nin', That mour-ners crave nae com-pa-ny, That mour-ners crave nae com-pa-ny.

Davie Stewart of Dundee: his tune of *The Dowie Dens of Yarrow*

INDEX OF TITLES AND FIRST LINES

(First lines are in italic)

168

GLOSSARY

adj. adjective; *adv.* adverb; *conj.* conjunction;
n. noun; *prep.* preposition; *pron.* pronoun; *v.* verb

Aa, aw *pron.* all
ablow *prep.* below
abeen, abune *prep.* above
ae *adj.* one
agee *adv.* to one side
aik *n.* oak
ain *adj.* own
aince *adv.* once
airt *n.* skill
ane *pron.* one
aneth *prep.* beneath

bailie *n.* cattleman
baith *pron.* both
balker *n.* horse that leaves bits of
land unploughed
baps *n.* soft bread rolls
beets, buits *n.* boots
ben *prep./ adv.* inside the house
billies *n.* farmhands
blate *adj.* shy
bleed, bluid *n.* blood
boddle *n.* twopence Scots
bothy *n.* outhouse
bowles, bowlies *n.* bowls
braw *adj.* handsome, fine
brawly *adv.* finely, well
bree *n.* stock
breet *n.* brute
brose *n.* oatmeal soaked in milk
buskit *v.* dressed
but and ben *n.* room and kitchen,
two-roomed house

caa, caw *v.* (i) call (ii) drive, work
caff *n.* chaff, straw
cankert *adj.* ill-natured
canny *adj.* careful, trustworthy

carpets *n.* slippers
castin (peats) *v.* digging or
cutting (peats)
chaff *n.* banter
chanty *n.* chamber-pot
chapped *v.* knocked
(chapped themselves away) (knocked to signal
for miners' cage to be lowered)
chatterie *adj.* broken
(chatterie rig) (strip of broken ground)
cheenge *v.* change
chiel *n.* man
chines *n.* chains
chow, chowin *v.* chew, chewing
claes *n.* clothes
compleen *v.* complain
conterie *n.* country
cottar *n.* married farmworker
cowp *v.* up-end
(cowp-the-ladle) (see-saw)
crackit *v.* chatted
craig *n.* crag
crans *n.* cranes

dashy *adj.* showy
dawtie *n.* darling
deem *n.* woman
deen *v.* done
dirl *v.* throb
div *v.* do
doddle *n.* male genitals
dother *n.* daughter
drouth *n.* thirst
duddies *n.* clothes
dune, deen *v.* done
durst *v.* dare
dwines *v.* wastes away

echt *n.* eight
een *n.* (i) eyes (ii) evening
eence *adv.* once
efterneen, efternune *n.* afternoon
eleiven *n.* eleven
eneuch *n./adj.* enough

faa *v.* fall
fail *n.* turf
(fail dyke) (turf wall)
fain *adv.* gladly
fairm, ferm *n.* farm
fan *conj.* when
fan *n.* winnowing device
(get three quarters throu the fan) (thresh three quarters of grain)
fat *pron.* what
fecht, fechter *n.* fight, fighter
fell *adj.* fierce
feerin *v.* ploughing
fere *n.* brother, comrade
file *n./conj.* while
fite *adj.* white
fleed *n.* flood
fleer *n.* floor
fleg *v.* scare
fore-anent *adj./n.* opposite
fun *v.* found
fur *prep./n.* (i) for (ii) a furrow

gaen, gane *v.* gone
gallus *adj.* good-looking (NE) bold, coarse (SW)
galshach *adj.* sweet
gars *v.* makes
gie *v.* give
gin *conj.* if
girse *n.* grass
glaur *n.* mud
glowered *v.* glared
gorblin *n.* infant or unfledged bird
gowan *n.* daisy

gowd *n.* gold
grat *v.* cried
gravat *n.* necktie
greet *v.* cry, weep
grieve, grievie *n.* foreman
growes *v.* grows
grun *n.* ground
guid, gweed *adj.* good
guidly *adj.* goodly
gweed-willie *adj.* good-natured
(gweed-willie chaff) (good-natured banter)
gyang *v.* go

haderums *n.* bagpipes
haill *adj.* whole
hairstin *v.* harvesting
hairt, hert *n.* heart
halflin *n.* half-grown boy
hashy *adj.* slapdash
haud awa *v.* keep away
hauders-on *n.* riveters' assistants
hauld *n.* land, property
hecht *v.* promised
heidie *n.* head
herry *v.* rob
het *adj.* hot
heuk *n.* hook
hielan walloch *n.* Highland fling (dance)
hit *pron.* it
hiz *pron.* us
hoddan an hose *n.* working men's clothes
hokey-pokey *n.* ice-cream cone
houms *n.* low-lying land by a river
howkin *v.* digging
(howkin deid) (digging up corpses)
hud *v.* had
humphy *adj.* humped
humpled, humplit *v.* hobbled

ilka, ilkae *adj./pron.* each

jalouses *v.* guesses
jine *v.* join

kaim *n.* comb
kebbuck *n.* cheese
kecklin *v.* cackling
ken, kennin *v.* know, knowing
kenspeckle *adj.* well-known
kinnen *n.* rabbit
kinnle *v.* kindle
kirk-yaird *n.* church-yard
kirn *n./ v.* churn
kitchie *n.* kitchen
kitchie deem *n.* cook (female)
kittle *v./adj.* (i) arouse (ii) nervous
(kittlet up his spunk) (took courage)
kittly *adj.* tickly
knappin *v.* breaking up (stones)
knowes *n.* knolls, hillocks
kye *n.* cattle

lane, leen *adj.* alone
(their lane, her leen) (their own, her own)
langsome *adj.* wearisome
lauchin *v.* laughing
lave (the) *n.* the rest, the others
leal-herted *adj.* loyal
lea *v.* leave
leg bail (gied them) run away (made them)
leman *n.* sweetheart
lift *n.* sky
linkin *v.* walking briskly
lippen tae *v.* trust to
loon *n.* boy
louss *n.* louse
lowe *n.* fire glow
lowsin, lowsing *n.* end of working day

maik *n.* match, equal
marrow *n.* mate, sweetheart
maun(na) *v.* must (not)
may n. maid
meal-pyocks *n.* oatmeal bags

minks *n.* tangles
mou *n.* mouth
mowe *v.* copulate with, make love to
muckle *adj./adv.* much, big

neist, neisten *adj.* next
neuk *n.* corner, fireside
nicky-tams *n.* strap or string tied round
trouser leg below knee

oor *adj./n.* (i) our (ii) hour
or *prep.* until
orra *adj.* spare, extra
(orra loon) (odd-job farm hand)
owsen *n.* oxen
owre *prep./adv.* (i) over (ii) too
(owre thrang) (too busy)

packman *n.* pedlar
pentit *adj.* painted
p'ints *n.* boot-laces
plack *n.* fourpence Scots
ploo *n.* plough
poke *n.* small bag
pooch *n.* pocket

queets *n.* ankles, fetlocks
quines *n.* girls

rade *v.* rode
rappit *v.* banged
redd on *v.* put on again
reek *n./v.* smoke, smell
reest *v.* praised
reid *adj.* red
rig (on the) making love
rivin *v.* tearing
rottans *n.* rats
roosed *v.* roused
rowed *v.* rolled

sall *v.* shall
samen *n.* same
sark *n.* shirt
sauf *v.* save
sautie *adj.* salty
sax *adj.* six
scartin *v.* scratching
schuil, skweel *n.* school
seik *v.* sick
seely court *n.* fairy court
seen, sune *adv.* soon
seiven *n.* seven
shaida *n.* shadow
sheen, shoon *n.* shoes
shew *v.* sew
sic *adj.* such
sinsyne *adv.* since
skeel *n.* skill
skimmer *n.* utensil for skimming milk
snap *v.* gobble (up)
sneck *v.* fasten
soger *n.* soldier
souter *n.* shoemaker
spad *n.* spade
speirt *v.* asked
spunk *n.* match
stap aboot *v.* get around
stappit fu *v.* stuffed full
staw *n.* dislike
steekit *v.* shut
steen, stane *n.* stone
steys *n.* corsets
stopping *n.* plug to block a mine shaft off
strachen *v.* straighten
straiked *v.* stroked
sweel *v.* pour

taen, tane *v.* took
(taen a staw) (took a dislike)
tamosher *n.* stomacher
tauld *v.* counted

tawse *n.* belt (in school)
teuchter *n.* countryman
the teen..the tither the one..the other
thirden *adj.* third
tho *conj.* though
thrang *adj.* busy
throu *prep.* through
tocher *n.* dowry
trachles *n.* toils
trysted *v.* made an appointment to meet
twined *v.* parted
tyawved *v.* tired out

waa *n.* wall
wad, wid *v.* would
wad *v.* married
wallie *adj.* china
wauken *v.* waken
waur *adj.* worse
weed *n.* clothes
weel-faured *adj.* good-looking
wey, wye *n.* way
whilies *adv.* now and then
whinny *adj.* furze-covered
whiskin *n.* hawking
wid, wud *n.* wood
win *n.* wind
wint *v.* want
wir *adj.* our
wrocht *v.* worked

yae *n./pron.* one
yestreen *n.* last night
yetts *n.* gates
yill *n.* ale
yin *pron.* one
yirn *v.* curdle

BIBLIOGRAPHY

Briggs, Katherine M.: *A Dictionary of British Folktales and Legends*, Routledge & Kegan Paul, London, 1977.

Brooksbank, Mary: *Sidlaw Breezes*, Dundee, reprinted David Winter, 1982.

Buchan, Norman: *101 Scottish Songs*, Collins 1962.

Buchan, Norman and Hall, Peter: *The Scottish Folksinger*, Collins, 1973.

Burns, Robert: *The Merry Muses of Caledonia*, 1800. Reprinted Macdonald, Edinburgh, 1982.

Chambers, Robert: *The Songs of Scotland Prior to Burns*, Edinburgh, 1862.

Child, Francis James: *The English and Scottish Popular Ballads*, Houghton, Miflin and Co. 1882–94, reprinted Dover Publications, New York, 1965.

Christie, Dean: *Traditional Ballad Airs*, 1876.

Douglas, Sheila: *The Sang's the Thing*, Polygon, Edinburgh, 1992.

Ford, Robert: *Vagabond Songs and Ballads of Scotland*, Alexander Gardner, Paisley, 1899.

Gatherer, Nigel: *Songs and Ballads of Dundee*, John Donald, Edinburgh, 1984.

Greig, Gavin and Duncan, James B.: *Folk Song Collection*, Vols. 1–4, AUP, Aberdeen; Vols. 5–8 to follow, Mercat Press, Edinburgh.

Harvey: *Harp of Stirlingshire*, date unknown.

Herd, David: *Ancient and Modern Scottish Songs*, 1776. Reprinted Scottish Academic Press, Edinburgh, 1973.

Herd Loon, A, (Rev. Robert H. Calder): *Lilts of the Lea-rig*, date unknown.

MacColl, Ewan: *Songs and Ballads of Scotland*, Oak Publications, New York; *Till Doomsday in the Afternoon*, MUP, 1986.

Munro, Ailie Edmunds: *The Folk Music Revival in Scotland*, Kahn & Averill, 1984. Reprinted Scottish Cultural Press, Aberdeen, 1995.

Ord, John: *Bothy Songs and Ballads*, Glasgow, 1930. Reprinted John Donald, Edinburgh, 1990.

Percy, Bishop Thomas: *Reliques of Ancient English Poetry*, London, 1765.

Poet's Box (Glasgow) Collection in the Mitchell Library, Glasgow.

Ramsay, Allan: *A Tea-table Miscellany*, Kilmarnock, 1778.

Scott, Sir Walter: *Minstrelsy of the Scottish Border*, Kelso, 1802–3.

Shepard, Leslie: *Chapbook Collection*.

Wedderburn: *The Complaynt of Scotland*, 1549.